The Open
University

INTRODUCTION TO DIVERSITY

EDITED BY IRENE RIDGE & CAROLINE M. POND

PHOTOS ON COVER ① ② ③ ④ ⑤

① *Volvox*

Photomicrograph of colonies of *Volvox* containing several asexually produced daughter colonies. The colony contains from hundreds to thousands of cells arranged at the surface of a watery matrix. The individual cells have two flagella and eyespots. They reproduce both asexually and sexually. Courtesy of Manfred Kage/Science Photo Library.

② Ammonite

Fossilized spiral shell of an ammonite, an extinct, squid-like cephalopod mollusc related to the living nautilus. Ammonites flourished from the Devonian period (400 million years ago) until becoming extinct at about the same time as the dinosaurs at the end of the Cretaceous (about 65 million years ago). Courtesy of Martin Bond/Science Photo Library.

③ Sea horse

X-ray (in false colours) of a sea horse, *Hippocampus* sp. A sea horse is a type of teleost fish. Sea horses swim slowly using fins (not seen here) and can use their tails to attach to seaweed or coral. The male sea horse incubates the fertilized eggs in a brood pouch on his abdomen. Courtesy of D. Roberts/Science Photo Library.

④ Sunflowers

A group of blooming sunflowers, *Helianthus* sp., against the sky. The plant produces composite flowers: the small, true flowers are clustered into a compact, round head which resembles a single flower. The plant is widely cultivated for its seeds which are used to make cooking oil and as food for livestock. Courtesy of David Nunuk/Science Photo Library.

⑤ Viruses

Illustration based on a transmission electron micrograph of human immunodeficiency viruses (HIV) (shown in yellow) budding out of a human T cell. HIV causes AIDS (Acquired Immune Deficiency Syndrome) by damaging T cells — the white blood cells that play a crucial role in the immune system. Courtesy of Chris Bjornberg/Science Photo Library.

The Open University, Walton Hall, Milton Keynes, MK7 6AA

First published 2001

Edited, designed and typeset by The Open University.

Printed in the United Kingdom by The Alden Group, Oxford.

ISBN 0 7492 9747 6

This publication forms part of an Open University course, S204 *Biology: Uniformity and Diversity*. The complete list of texts which make up this course can be found at the back. Details of this and other Open University courses can be obtained from the Call Centre, PO Box 724, The Open University, Milton Keynes MK7 6ZS, United Kingdom: tel. +44 (0)1908 653231, e-mail ces-gen@open.ac.uk

Alternatively, you may visit the Open University website at http://www.open.ac.uk where you can learn more about the wide range of courses and packs offered at all levels by The Open University.

To purchase this publication or other components of Open University courses, contact Open University Worldwide Ltd, The Berrill Building, Walton Hall, Milton Keynes MK7 6AA, United Kingdom: tel. +44 (0)1908 858785; fax +44 (0)1908 858787; e-mail ouwenq@open.ac.uk; website http://www.ouw.co.uk

1.1

s204book 1i1.1

THE S204 COURSE TEAM

COURSE TEAM CHAIR
HILARY MACQUEEN

ACADEMIC EDITOR
CAROLINE POND

COURSE MANAGERS
VIVIEN BACIGALUPO
CHRIS EDWARDS
CHRISTINE GORMAN

COURSE SECRETARY
DAWN PARTNER

AUTHORS
MARY BELL (BOOK 5)
ERIC BOWERS (BOOK 6)
JOHN BURNETT (BOOK 4)
ALAN CANN (BOOK 4)
MEL CLEMENTS (BOOK 3)
BASIRO DAVEY (BOOK 2)
HILARY DENNY (BOOK 5)
SUE DOWNS (BOOK 5)
MANDY DYSON (BOOKS 2 AND 6)
ANNA FURTH (BOOKS 3 AND 4)
MIKE GILLMAN (BOOK 2)
TIM HALLIDAY (BOOK 2)
JANE LOUGHLIN (BOOK 3)
DAVID MALE (BOOK 4)
HILARY MACQUEEN (BOOK 4)
JUDITH METCALFE (BOOK 3)
PAUL O'SHEA (BOOK 3)
PHIL PARKER (BOOK 5)
CAROLINE POND (BOOKS 1, 2 AND 6)
IRENE RIDGE (BOOKS 1, 4 AND 5)
JERRY ROBERTS (BOOK 5)
DAVID ROBINSON (BOOK 6)
JILL SAFFREY (BOOK 3)
ROBERT SAUNDERS (BOOK 6)
AYONA SILVA-FLETCHER (BOOK 3)
VALDA STEVENS (BOOK 2)
MARGARET SWITHENBY (BOOKS 3 AND 4)
COLIN WALKER (BOOKS 3 AND 4)

GLO EDITOR
PEGGY VARLEY

EDITORS
IAN NUTTALL
GILLIAN RILEY
BINA SHARMA
MARGARET SWITHENBY

OU GRAPHIC DESIGN
RUTH DRAGE
PAM OWEN
HOWARD TWINER
ANDREW WHITEHEAD

CD-ROM AND VIDEO PRODUCTION
GAYLE BLOCK
JACKI BROWN
PHIL BUTCHER
HILARY DENNY
MIKE DODD
PHIL GAURON
CARYL HOOPER
G. D. JAYALAKSHMI
JULIET KAUFFMANN
MARTIN KEMP
MARK MURPHY
DAVID ROBINSON
LIZ SUGDEN
ANDREW SUTTON
GARY TUCKNOTT
VERINA WAIGHTS
DARREN WYCHERLEY

LIBRARY
LYDIA EATON
JUDY THOMAS

PICTURE RESEARCH
LYDIA EATON

BOOK ASSESSORS
GIANFRANCO NOVARINO (BOOK 1)
AUBREY MANNING (BOOK 2)
KARL SWANN AND DAVID HARRIS (BOOK 3)
PETER WHITE (BOOK 4)
DAVID CLARKSON AND RACHEL LEECH (BOOK 5)
JOHN CURREY AND BRIAN JAMES (BOOK 6)

EXTERNAL COURSE ASSESSOR
PROFESSOR SIR DAVID SMITH

CONSULTANTS
PATRICIA ASH
SUE DOWNS
CHRISTINE GORMAN
JEAN MACQUEEN
TERRY WHATSON

SKILLS
PATRICIA ASH
HILARY DENNY

CONTENTS

CHAPTER 1   ORDERING DIVERSITY   1

IRENE RIDGE

1.1 INTRODUCTION: TYPES OF DIVERSITY 1
1.2   SPECIES AND FAMILY TREES: ORDERING DIVERSITY 6
1.3 THE DOMAINS OF LIFE 19
1.4 THE PROKARYOTIC KINGDOMS 23
1.5 THE EUKARYOTIC KINGDOMS 29
REFERENCES 53
FURTHER READING 53

CHAPTER 2   DIVERSITY IN PROTOCTISTS   55

IRENE RIDGE

2.1 INTRODUCTION: INNOVATION AND OPPORTUNITY 55
2.2 METABOLIC INNOVATION 60
2.3 MOTILITY AND FEEDING 63
2.4 PROTECTION AND SUPPORT 69
2.5 MULTICELLULARITY, SIZE AND SHAPE 75
2.6 AN OVERVIEW OF PROTOCTIST DIVERSITY: SEX, LIFE CYCLES
      AND SYMBIOSIS 82
FURTHER READING 92

CHAPTER 3   BIOLOGICAL INVESTIGATION   93

CAROLINE POND

3.1 INTRODUCTION 93
3.2 HYPOTHESES AND THEORIES 93
3.3 OBSERVATIONS 98
3.4 EXPERIMENTS 99
3.5 LABORATORY ORGANISMS 105
3.6 PLANNING AND INTERPRETING EXPERIMENTS 119
3.7 CONCLUSIONS 129
REFERENCES AND FURTHER READING 130

ACKNOWLEDGEMENTS   131

INDEX   133

ORDERING DIVERSITY

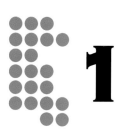

1.1 INTRODUCTION: TYPES OF DIVERSITY

At the centre of biology are the complementary themes of biological diversity and uniformity. Think first about what the diversity of life means to you.

○ Consider your local environment (which can be your room, the area viewed from the window, or the whole neighbourhood) and list at least three organisms or types of organisms that you think illustrate diversity.

● You might have listed robin, blue tit and great tit — three *species* of birds that visit bird tables in Britain — and, indeed, the number of species in a given area is often used as a measure of diversity. Or you might have listed broad *types* of organisms such as plants, animals, fungi or bacteria (which are everywhere, including the skin, mouth, gut, etc. of human bodies), demonstrating the variety of structure and ways of life. It would be equally valid to list *communities* of organisms or ecosystems: the soil community, a lawn or pasture, a woodland, or even the bacterial community of the gut. The point is that biological diversity (or **biodiversity** as it is now commonly called) can be thought of in many different ways.

Now read the following extracts inspired by a night-time storm in the Amazonian rainforest. As you read, note down the organisms mentioned. You may not recognize a number of the organisms. Don't worry about this, but concentrate on the diversity described and try to identify different *types* of diversity.

> The lightning bolts were acting like strobe flashes to illuminate the wall of the rain forest. At intervals I glimpsed the storied structure: top canopy 30 meters off the ground, middle trees spread raggedly below that, and a lowermost scattering of shrubs and small trees. The forest was framed for a few moments in this theatrical setting. Its image turned surreal, projected into the unbounded wilderness of the human imagination, thrown back in time 10 000 years. Somewhere close I knew spear-nosed bats flew in the tree crowns in search of fruit, palm vipers coiled in ambush in the roots of orchids, jaguars walked the river's edge; around them eight hundred species of trees stood, more than are native to all of North America; and a thousand species of butterflies, 6 per cent of the entire world fauna, waited for the dawn.

> About the orchids of that place we knew very little. About flies and beetles almost nothing, fungi nothing, most kinds of organisms nothing. Five thousand kinds of bacteria might be found in a pinch of soil, and about them we knew absolutely nothing.

> The storm arrived, racing from the forest's edge, turning from scattered splashing drops into sheets of water driven by gusts of wind.

It forced me back into the shelter of the corrugated iron roof of the open-air living quarters, where I sat and waited with the mateiros. The men stripped off their clothing and walked out into the open, soaping and rinsing themselves in the torrential rain, laughing and singing. In bizarre counterpoint, leptodactylid frogs struck up a loud and monotonous honking on the forest floor close by. I wondered where they had been during the day. I had never encountered a single one while sifting through the vegetation and rotting debris on sunny days, in habitats they are supposed to prefer.

Farther out, a kilometer or two away, a troop of red howler monkeys chimed in, their chorus one of the strangest sounds to be heard in all of nature, as enthralling in its way as the songs of humpback whales. A male opened with an accelerating series of deep grunts, expanding into prolonged roars and was then joined by the higher-pitched call of the females. This far away, filtered through dense foliage, the full chorus was machine-like: deep, droning, metallic.

Such raintime calls are usually territorial advertisements, the means by which the animals space themselves out and control enough land to forage and breed.

… Animals and plants have come to use heavy rains and floods routinely to time episodes in their life cycle. They threaten rivals, mate, hunt prey, lay eggs in new water pools, and dig shelters in the rain-softened earth.

On a larger scale, the storms drive change in the whole structure of the forest. The natural dynamism raises the diversity of life by means of local destruction and regeneration.

Somewhere a large horizontal tree limb is weak and vulnerable, covered by a dense garden of orchids, bromeliads, and other kinds of plants that grow on trees. The rain fills up the cavities enclosed by the axil sheaths of the epiphytes and soaks the humus and clotted dust around their roots. After years of growth the weight has become nearly unsupportable. A gust of wind whips through or lightening strikes the tree trunk, and the limb breaks and plummets down, clearing a path to the ground …

… the fallen trees and branches rot and crumble, offering hiding places and food to a vast array of basidiomycete fungi, slime moulds, ants, beetles, earwigs, springtails, real scorpions, and other forms that live mostly or exclusively in this habitat. They add thousands of species to the diversity of the primary forest.

(Extracts from Chapter 1, *The Diversity of Life,* E. O. Wilson, 1994)

Figure 1.1 illustrates some of the organisms mentioned in the extract.

Figure 1.1 Organisms from the Amazonian rainforest.

(a) jaguar, *Panthera onca*.

(d) ground beetle.

(e) epiphytic orchid, *Masdevallia strobelii*.

(b) red howler monkey, *Alouatta seniculus*.

(f) bromeliad, *Nidularium* sp.

(c) owl butterfly, *Caligo teucer*.

(g) coral fungus growing on the rainforest floor.

There is certainly a huge diversity of species in the Amazonian rainforest (at least 800 species of trees and over 3000 species of butterflies, for example) but there is also diversity of growth form among animals and plants (e.g. trees of three heights and non-woody plants growing on the trees); of behaviour among animals (the nocturnal frogs and the day-flying butterflies); and of communities *within* the

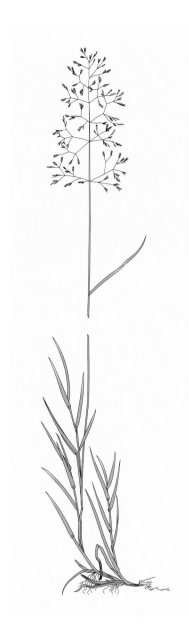

Figure 1.2   Common bent-grass, *Agrostis capillaris*.

forest (the plant garden on the tree limb and the community that develops on the fallen, rotting limb). You may have thought of other types of diversity but probably all relate to things that can be *seen* at one point in time. However, 95% of species that have ever existed are now extinct and we know of their existence only from fossil evidence. So modern, visible biodiversity is only the tip of the iceberg. In addition, a vast amount of biodiversity is *invisible*, because it occurs at the level of genes, molecules or processes within organisms. Much of this study area concerns genetic, molecular and physiological diversity, so we describe one example below to illustrate the nature of each and also the links to ecology.

1.1.1 HIDDEN DIVERSITY: HEAVY METAL TOLERANCE IN A GRASS

When present in soil at high concentrations, metals such as copper, lead or zinc (commonly referred to as *heavy metals*) are toxic to most plants. Soils containing such metals may occur naturally, but in the UK they are more commonly produced by industrial pollution or as the spoil heaps of mines. New spoil heaps may remain bare of vegetation for years but gradually they are colonized by plants (usually grasses) that look identical to those in surrounding vegetation. Common bent-grass (*Agrostis capillaris*) (see Figure 1.2) is an early colonizer. If common bent-grass from 'normal' soil is transplanted to a toxic soil, it nearly always dies. However, seed from common bent-grass growing on toxic soil produces seedlings that survive on that soil.

○   Suggest an explanation for the above observations on common bent-grass. Why is it able to colonize soils rich in heavy metals?

●   The bent-grass growing on the toxic soil must be tolerant of these conditions (or you could say resistant to the heavy metals present) and this tolerance, or resistance, must be conferred by genes that are not present in the majority of plants growing on 'normal' soil. The fact that progeny (seedlings) from plants on toxic soil are able to grow on that soil is evidence of a heritable (i.e. genetic) basis for tolerance.

Within the common bent-grass species, therefore, populations exist which are genetically distinct. Individuals from these populations *look* identical to other members of the species but differ *ecologically* because they are able to grow on a soil from which others are excluded and this ecological difference is based on genetic differences that confer different biochemical and physiological properties. Genetic variation of this kind between populations within a species is an important aspect of biodiversity.

There is another lesson to be learnt from the common bent-grass example that concerns *types of explanation*. The question asked was the sort that an ecologist or physiologist might pose: 'Why does common bent-grass grow in these conditions?' And the answer was in terms of *properties that the organism possesses*: it has certain genes that confer certain physiological properties which confer resistance to heavy metals. This sort of answer is described as a **proximate explanation** because it relates to the here and now and to *how* an organism does something. Another sort of question might be asked by an evolutionary biologist:

'Why and by what process have these metal-resistant grasses come to dominate the population on toxic soils?' This sort of question requires a different kind of answer, one that is described as an **ultimate explanation** because it relates to evolutionary processes that occurred in the past.

To provide such an ultimate explanation in this example requires additional information. We return to it in Chapter 3 but, in brief: genes for heavy metal tolerance do occur with very low frequency in common bent-grass populations on normal soil but metal-tolerant individuals grow poorly there in competition with non-tolerant plants and tend to be removed by natural selection. However, if metal-tolerant plants spread, by chance, to toxic soils, they have a powerful advantage, are favoured by natural selection and survive to found a new population.

From this ultimate explanation it can be seen that the ability of organisms to adapt to new or altered conditions depends on the existence of genetic variation between individuals in a population. Such variation can be transformed, through natural selection, into population diversity which, in the longer term, is the raw material from which new species may evolve. For these kinds of reasons, attention is now being focused not just on conserving 'a species' but on conserving genetic and often hidden diversity *within* species.

A general *definition of biodiversity* encompassing all the types mentioned above was suggested by E. O. Wilson in 1997:

> … all hereditarily based variation at all levels of organization, from the genes within a single local population or species, to the species composing all or part of a local community, and finally to the communities themselves that compose the living parts of the multifarious ecosystems of the world.

Here we give most attention to variation between species within each of three broad groups — microbes, plants and animals — to illustrate the many ways in which organisms have adapted to a vast range of environments. You need to remember, however, that underlying this diversity there are fundamental *similarities* between all organisms. This common core to life involves properties and processes at the level of whole organisms, natural selection being one example; and properties at the level of cells and molecules. The accepted explanation for biological uniformity is that life on Earth probably evolved from a single common ancestor.

○ As a revision exercise of earlier studies, list at least three properties or characteristics common to all living organisms.

● Living organisms (1) consist of one or more *cells* which are (2) surrounded by a *membrane*, and (3) use the same kinds of carbon-based macromolecules as basic components (proteins, fats, carbohydrates and nucleic acids). All organisms (4) reproduce and use DNA as their genetic material; (5) decode DNA into proteins in a similar way; and (6) require a constant supply of energy in order to survive and reproduce. At the cellular level, energy is most commonly provided as ATP.

Whether talking about uniformity or (especially) diversity, however, an essential requirement in biology is a system for *naming and classifying* organisms. Scientific names provide the language by which people communicate about biodiversity; a classification system, like a family tree, can give information about how organisms are related to each other and the common properties shared by different groups. Systems for naming and classifying organisms are the subject of Section 1.2. Later sections provide a broad framework for classifying organisms and look at the definitions and general characteristics of major groups. The largest grouping, *domains*, is considered in Section 1.3 and the next largest, *kingdoms*, in Sections 1.4 and 1.5. You should then appreciate the significance of describing something as a 'bacterium', a 'fungus' or an 'animal' and be able to start exploring for yourself the diversity within these large groups that is illustrated on the *Guide to Living Organisms* (*GLO*) CD-ROM.

SUMMARY OF SECTION 1.1

1   Biological diversity or biodiversity has many aspects which include genetic, biochemical, physiological, structural, taxonomic and ecological components.

2   Diversity at the genetic and molecular levels is often hidden (with no visible, e.g. structural, counterpart) but may be linked to ecological or physiological diversity. Populations of common bent-grass tolerant of one or more heavy metals and growing on toxic soils such as mine spoil-heaps provide one example of hidden diversity.

3   The uniformity of life is reflected in a common core of properties at the level of whole organisms and of cells and molecules.

4   Biologists may ask two sorts of questions which require different kinds of explanations. 'How' questions (usually asked by ecologists, physiologists and biochemists) require a proximate explanation; 'why' questions (usually asked by evolutionary biologists) require an ultimate explanation in terms of genetic properties and evolutionary processes.

1.2   SPECIES AND FAMILY TREES: ORDERING DIVERSITY

To study biological diversity, it is first necessary to identify organisms, which means classifying them into universally recognized groups or **taxa** (singular, **taxon**) and giving each taxon a universally recognized name. Biologists who name and classify organisms are described as **taxonomists**.

○   From earlier studies, what is the smallest taxon in common usage?

●   The species.

Species are the base units of taxonomy and, as mentioned in Section 1.1, the biodiversity of an area is commonly assessed in terms of the number of species present. Currently about 1.8 million species have been properly described, although estimates of the total number range from 5 to 100 million, with 30 million being a widely accepted figure. With such enormous diversity of extant species, we have to ask how taxonomists decide whether two organisms belong to the same species — what *is* a species?

1.2.1 WHAT IS A SPECIES?

This question is neither trivial nor easy to answer. Members of a species are not genetically identical (recall Section 1.1.1) but they share many genes and the level of genetic identity usually accepted as sufficient to classify two organisms in the same species is that they can *interbreed*. The **biological definition of a species** is thus 'a group of organisms that actually or potentially interbreed to produce fertile offspring'. The logic behind this definition is that it supposedly identifies a group of closely related organisms that evolved from a common ancestor, which is described as a **natural classification**. It is quite possible to classify organisms in other ways to produce an unnatural or **artificial classification**, usually for some specific purpose. For example, some gardening books group plants on the basis of height and flower colour, which is useful when designing a garden but of little use to a biologist. Notice that individual species are given their generic Latin names followed by the abbreviation 'sp.', for example, *Limax* sp., indicating one of several slug species in the genus *Limax* (plural, 'spp.').

○ Look at Figure 1.3 but DON'T read the legend. Group the butterflies illustrated into two species on the basis of their appearance.

● Figure 1.3a shows one species (a male of the Southern Festoon, *Zerynthia polyxena*) and (b), (c) and (d) are all members of a second species, the Spanish Festoon, *Zerynthia rumina*. (b) shows a male of a variety (or forma) called *Z. rumina* forma *medesicaste*; (c) shows a female of another colour variety; and (d) shows a female of *Z. rumina* subspecies *ornatior* forma *canteneri*, which is particularly large. Butterflies are often (as here) very difficult to classify correctly into biological species when comparisons are based solely on outward appearances.

The problem with the biological definition of a species is that, unfortunately, it is often difficult or impossible to apply. Extinct organisms known only from fossils and organisms that reproduce only asexually (which applies to some plants and single-celled organisms) are obvious examples. There are practical problems too. It is simply not possible to carry out breeding tests on collections of beetles obtained with great difficulty from the canopy of a tropical rainforest and transported as preserved specimens to a taxonomist working in a museum thousands of miles away. Of necessity, many taxonomists have to work with dead specimens and separate one species from another on the basis of differences in *appearance*, including external structure and internal anatomy.

Increasingly, differences in chemical make-up, chromosome structure, ecology and behaviour are taken into account when delineating species but the crucial breeding tests are still only rarely performed. Inevitably, confusion and problems arise.

(a)

(b)

(c)

(d)

Figure 1.3 The upper wing surfaces of two species of festoon butterflies (*Zerynthia* spp.): (a) Southern Festoon, *Zerynthia polyxena*; (b) Spanish Festoon, *Zerynthia rumina* forma *medesicaste*; (c) Spanish Festoon, *Zerynthia rumina*, another colour variety; (d) Spanish Festoon, *Zerynthia rumina*, subspecies *ornatior* forma *canteneri*. All are drawn to the same scale.

PROBLEMS IN CLASSIFYING SPECIES

Given that, usually, species *must* be delimited on the basis of structure, two closely linked problems arise, one biological and the other human. The biological problem is that species differ greatly in the amount of variation *within* and *between* them. At one extreme are species such as the Hawaiian tree *Metrosideros polymorpha* which shows astonishing variation in both structure and ecology.

(a)

(b)

(c)

Figure 1.4 Variation in the Hawaiian tree *Metrosideros polymorpha*. (a) Fully grown tree, height approximately 30 m; (b) fully grown tree, approximately 2 m tall with red flowers; (c) tree with yellow flower to illustrate flower variation.

Some of this variation is illustrated in Figure 1.4. *Metrosideros* grows in mountain swamps, as a colonizer on volcanic lava, and in lowland tropical rainforest, ranging in height from one to over thirty metres; even adjacent trees may vary in flower colour, leaf colour and hairiness and many other characters and all these different forms appear to interbreed freely.

At the other extreme there are species of plants which look almost indistinguishable but are only distantly related and are genetically very different (Figure 1.5). When distantly related organisms come to resemble each other closely the process involved is described as **convergent evolution**; you will meet more examples of this later.

The human problem is that taxonomists frequently disagree about the degree of morphological (or molecular) difference that is necessary to separate two species. At one extreme are the 'splitters', who may define dozens of species separated by only minute differences; and at the other extreme are 'lumpers' who would classify all these organisms within one, variable species. If there were no evidence of interbreeding, *Metrosideros polymorpha* would undoubtedly be classified as several species by 'splitters'. Fossils in the hominid lineage (the ancestors of the human species) also illustrate the lumpers/splitters dichotomy: palaeontologists who hunt for fossils in the field tend to emphasize the unique

(a)

(b)

features of 'their' fossils and give them new names, whereas museum taxonomists who look at several fossils together, tend to emphasize similarities and group them together under one name.

Accurate identification of species is vital not only for making inventories of biodiversity but also for very practical reasons, especially in relation to agricultural pests. This last point is well illustrated by the African mealy-bug that devastated coffee crops in Kenya for many years. The bug was identified as a Kenyan species and years of effort went into finding its natural enemies and testing them as possible agents for biological control. None of the natural enemies of the Kenyan species had any effect on the pest. At this point a taxonomist became involved and showed that the pest was actually a different species, formerly restricted to Uganda. Natural enemies of the *correct* species were identified in Uganda, introduced to Kenya, and within a few years the pest mealy-bug became rare. Millions of pounds were wasted in research and lost crops because of the initial incorrect identification of the mealy-bug species.

Figure 1.5 Similarities in external appearance between distantly related species of desert plants. (a) A cactus (family Cactaceae) from North America; (b) a spurge (family Euphorbiaceae) from Africa.

SPECIAL PROBLEMS WITH MICROBES

The problem of defining and identifying species is especially acute for microbes, that is, prokaryotes (organisms which lack a membrane-bound nucleus and organelles) and some fungi, which are all structurally simple and often similar. Here are a few examples that illustrate the nature of the problem. Commonly there are few, if any, structural markers so that microbial species are identified by what they *do* (e.g. what disease they cause or what substances they break down) and also by chemical properties (e.g. of cell walls or membranes). In addition, if sexual reproduction occurs at all, it is 'unconventional': in prokaryotes, for example, instead of mixing up entire genomes by fusion plus meiosis, small parts of genomes may be transferred from one cell to another. Such **gene transfer** occurs not only between members of the same species but also between *different* species, and here lies the explanation for the alarming spread of antibiotic resistance through many types of bacteria. Bacteria spread their genes around in a remarkably promiscuous way so that the biological species concept breaks down and the boundaries between 'species' become blurred.

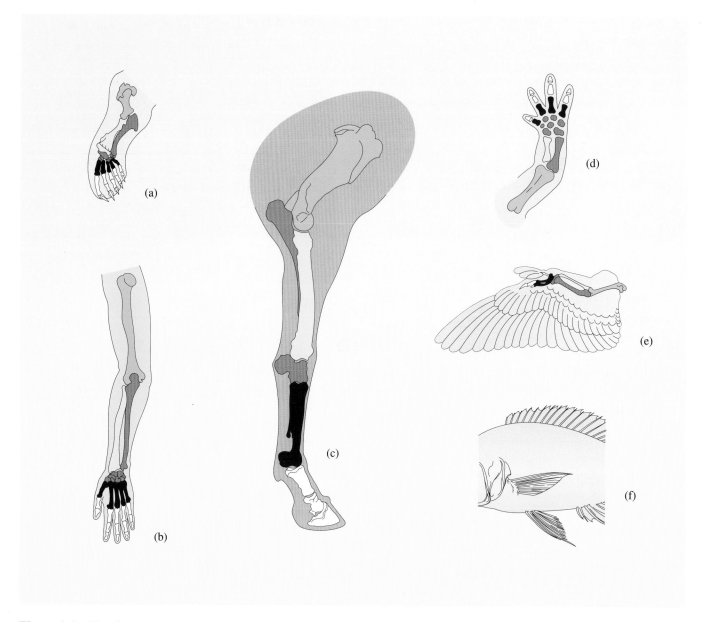

Figure 1.6 Vertebrate appendages showing the skeletal support. (a) seal's flipper; (b) human arm; (c) horse's leg; (d) amphibian's leg; (e) bird's wing; (f) cichlid (teleost) fish fin. Corresponding limb structures are shown in similar shading.

1.2.2 HIGHER ORDER TAXA AND THE TAXONOMIC HIERARCHY

Identifying and naming species is just the first step in creating order out of biological diversity. Species are grouped into **genera** (singular, **genus**), genera into families and so on, to give a hierarchy of taxa. For a natural classification that reflects evolutionary relationships, all the taxa grouped together *must have a common ancestor*, which means that they share certain characteristics. The characteristics that are used to infer common descent are described as **homologous** and since this concept of homology underpins natural classification, we shall examine it more closely.

○ Figure 1.6 shows a range of vertebrate appendages. Which ones appear to be homologous?

● All except the fin of the teleost fish are homologous because the plan of the underlying skeleton is basically similar, indicating a common origin. The fish fin is not homologous, even though it looks somewhat similar to a seal flipper, because the bony fin rays that support it are arranged quite differently from the bones in the other appendages.

The example above demonstrates that homologous structures do not necessarily perform the same function. Structures that perform similar functions, look superficially similar but have *different* origins (like the fish fin and seal flipper, or the wings of an insect and a bird) are described as **analogous**.

The concept of homology applies not only to whole-body structures but also to macromolecules, such as proteins and nucleic acids. In such molecules, 'structure' means sequence of amino acids or nucleotide bases respectively, and we describe later how molecular sequence data can be used to sort out the boundaries of higher taxa and the evolutionary relationships between large groups.

NAMES AND THE TAXONOMIC HIERARCHY

We mentioned in Section 1.1 the importance of giving each species a unique name and that name is a **binomial** (meaning two words). The origins of this system and the derivation of names from Greek or Latin are described in the Study File instructions for using *GLO*. Creeping buttercup, for example, is *Ranunculus repens*, the first name being that of the genus and the second defining a particular species within the genus. Thus *Ranunculus acris* is the meadow buttercup, *R. bulbosus* (abbreviating the generic name to its first letter) the bulbous buttercup — and there are many other buttercups, all of them species with yellow flowers in the genus *Ranunculus* (Figure 1.7). Notice that the Latin name of a species is always written in italics (or underlined if handwritten), with the name of the genus having an initial capital letter. To be absolutely correct, the Latin name of a species should be followed by the name (*not* in italics) of the person who first described that species. For example, the broad bean and brown trout, both first described by Linnaeus (who is commonly abbreviated to L.) are *Vicia faba* L. and *Salmo trutta* L., respectively.

(a)   (b)   (c)

Figure 1.7 Three species of buttercup, *Ranunculus* spp. (a) meadow buttercup, *Ranunculus acris*, (b) bulbous buttercup, *Ranunculus bulbosus*, (c) creeping buttercup, *Ranunculus repens*.

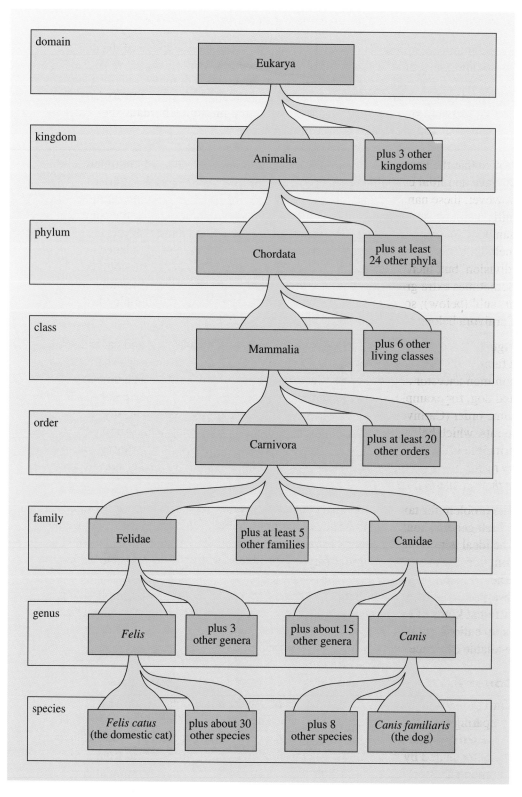

Figure 1.8   The classification of the domestic cat and dog illustrating the taxonomic hierarchy up to domain level.

To revise the names of higher taxonomic groups, study Figure 1.8.

○ Beginning at species level, give the full taxonomic description of the dog up to domain level.

● The dog, *Canis familiaris*, belongs to the genus *Canis*, in the **family** Canidae, the **order** Carnivora, the **class** Mammalia, the **phylum** Chordata, the **kingdom** Animalia and the **domain** Eukarya.

Notice that the names of higher taxonomic categories are not written in italics but do have an initial capital letter when the latinized names are used. Often, however, these names are anglicized, for example, Animalia becomes animals (no initial capital), and Mammalia becomes mammals but, confusingly, the common name for Bacteria is 'bacteria' and is often used to mean any prokaryote, including Archaea. In the plant kingdom, the term 'phylum' was replaced by 'division' but, increasingly, this term is being abandoned and we do not use it. Sometimes extra groupings are included using the prefix 'super' (meaning above) or 'sub' (below); so there can be a superorder or subclass. For example, the Carnivora belong to the subclass Eutheria (placentals).

Figure 1.8 can be looked at as a simplified family tree of the dog and cat and such a family tree is called a **phylogeny**. It shows at what level two groups share a common ancestor and, therefore, their evolutionary relationship. The domestic cat and dog, for example, share a common ancestor at order level: they belong to the same order (Carnivora) and are, therefore, more closely related than, say, dogs are to rats, which belong to the order Rodentia in the class Mammalia. An important principle is illustrated by this example: *the higher the taxonomic category shared by two organisms, the more distant their relationship and the further back in time is their common ancestor*.

The problem for taxonomists is how to decide on the boundaries of higher taxa — which genera should be included in this family, which families in this order, etc. The ideal is to group together in one category organisms that have a single common ancestor (i.e. are **monophyletic**) and are more closely related to each other than to organisms in any other category. But taxonomists inevitably disagree about these groupings, interpreting evidence differently or emphasizing different kinds of evidence. So phylogenies and higher taxa are not so much facts as inventions of taxonomists, based on their informed opinions and the best available evidence. We consider next the nature of some of this evidence.

CONSTRUCTING PHYLOGENIES: EVIDENCE AND PROBLEMS

Until the 1980s, phylogenies and higher taxa were constructed mainly by comparing the structure and physiology of organisms. *Homologous* characteristics had to be compared and decisions made about whether a particular character shared by two groups was *primitive* (reflecting their origin from a common ancestor) or *derived* (having evolved separately in each group after separation from a common ancestor). Such decisions and distinguishing homology from analogy are not always easy so that, inevitably, there were many disagreements among taxonomists. It was a long held view, for example, that

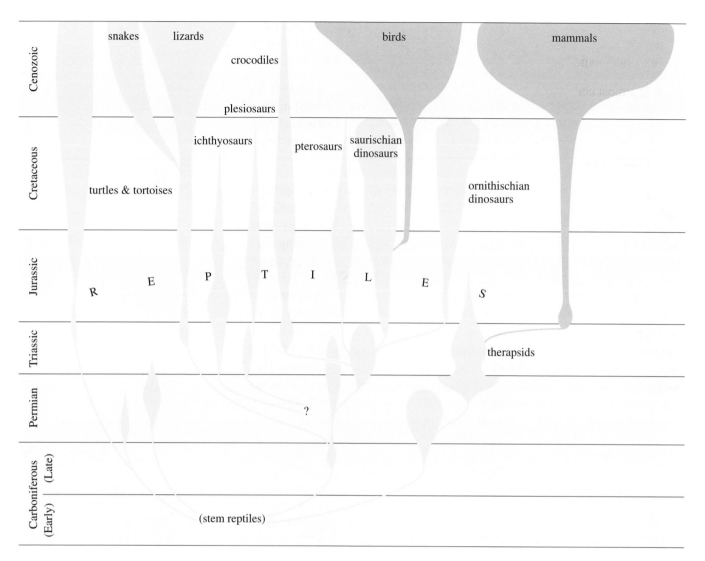

Figure 1.9 Phylogeny of reptiles, birds and mammals. The width of a group indicates the approximate number of species. The question mark indicates uncertainty about origin.

birds and mammals are more closely related to each other than to any reptile and had evolved from a common, 'warm-blooded' ancestor. Figure 1.9 shows the modern consensus about the phylogeny of reptiles, birds and mammals according to which birds are actually more closely related to crocodiles than to mammals.

○ Mammals are grouped at the taxonomic rank of a class. According to Figure 1.9, how should reptiles and birds be grouped to give two equivalent, monophyletic classes?

● One class would contain the turtles and tortoises and the second all the other reptiles plus birds! This conclusion follows from Figure 1.9 because each of these classes has, like the mammals, a single common ancestor among the ancient or stem reptiles in the early Carboniferous period. The fact that, in most textbooks and museums, birds and reptiles are placed in separate classes reflects an older taxonomy and human reluctance to alter long-established groupings.

○ From Figure 1.9, is 'warm-bloodedness' (more correctly, homeothermy — maintaining a constant body temperature) a primitive or derived character in birds and mammals?

● It is almost certainly a derived character, which evolved separately in birds and mammals. Otherwise the character would have been present in the ancient stem reptiles and *lost* in all the living reptiles, which seems very unlikely. We cannot be sure, however, because evidence of homeothermy is difficult to detect in fossils.

The time dimension for the phylogeny in Figure 1.9, for example, deciding *when* snakes evolved from lizards and mammals from therapsid reptiles, and also deciding whether a character is primitive or derived comes from fossil evidence. Incomplete though it is, fossil evidence has played a key role in sorting out the phylogenies of vertebrates, but the same is not true for many other groups of animals, or for plants, fungi and most of the unicellular organisms. In these groups, fossils are mostly rare or completely absent and, since the 1980s, *molecular evidence* from extant organisms has been used increasingly to sort out the higher taxa. For the prokaryotes in particular, molecular sequence comparisons have revolutionized taxonomy and led to recognition of the oldest and most fundamental division of living organisms into three **domains**: Bacteria, Archaea and Eukarya, which are discussed further in Section 1.3. The principles of using molecular sequence data to measure relatedness between organisms are described in Box 1.1, which you should study carefully.

BOX 1.1   MAPPING ANCIENT FAMILY TREES: MOLECULAR SEQUENCING AND PHYLOGENY

To work out a phylogeny for organisms that diverged very far back in time (in fact close to the origin of life for the domains), scientists compare the sequence of units in molecules such as proteins or nucleic acids and measure how similar they are. The molecules compared must be carefully chosen for the following reasons:

• they must *perform the same function in all the organisms*, that is, be homologous, so that 'like is compared with like'. For example, a particular kind of ribosomal RNA can be compared only with exactly the same kind of ribosomal RNA — and not with transfer RNA or any other sort of RNA.

• they must have *changed relatively little over time* as a result of mutations, that is, be *highly conserved*. All DNA (and hence the RNA derived from it and the proteins translated from the RNA) is subject to constant random change — mutation — which alters the sequence of units (bases and amino acids). If a change results in serious malfunctioning of the molecule, it is eliminated because the organisms in which it occurs fail to develop or breed. But if a change has no deleterious consequences or even

improves molecular function, it can persist and spread through a population as the organisms carrying it reproduce. Many proteins have changed a great deal, often assuming different functions, so they are useless for broad comparisons between, for example, eukaryotes and prokaryotes.

Very few molecules meet both of the criteria described above but among the most useful are cytochrome c (a protein involved in respiration) and, especially, ribosomal (r) RNA from the small or large subunit of ribosomes. To compare rRNAs you first need to know the base sequence, and usually the sequence in the DNA specifying the RNA that is being used (called ribosomal DNA, or rDNA). Then the molecules are aligned so that there is *maximum similarity* of sequence; this step is necessary because extra bits may have been added (or sections deleted) over evolutionary time, especially to the beginning or end of a molecule, and only the most closely matching zones are truly homologous. In Figure 1.10a, an 18-base stretch of DNA that codes for part of an rRNA molecule (1a) is aligned for maximum similarity assuming that extra bases have been added at the start. Without alignment (1b, second row), the molecules appear very dissimilar, having only 33% matching bases; but once aligned (1c, third row), identical stretches of DNA are identified. In Figure 1.10b, three 18-base stretches of rDNA (from Eukarya, Archaea and Bacteria) are compared after alignment for maximum similarity and the similarity in base sequence of homologous zones is measured. You can see that 12 of the 18 bases in (2) are the same as in (1) so that there is a 67% similarity, whereas (1) and (3) are only 33% similar.

○ What is the percentage similarity between (2) and (3)?

● 9 bases are the same, so there is a 50% similarity.

What this result would imply is that (1) Eukarya, are most closely related to (2) Archaea; and Archaea are more closely related to Eukarya than to (3) Bacteria. In practice, sequences comprising hundreds of bases must be compared (using a computer) and statistical tests must be used to assess the probability that base similarities are not due purely to chance. Such large-scale analyses confirm the above conclusions about relationships between domains.

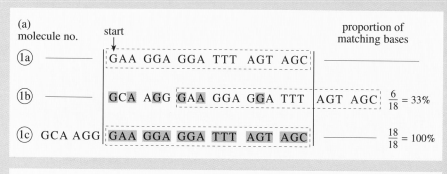

Figure 1.10 Hypothetical base sequences for short stretches of DNA that code for rRNA. (a) Alignment to find the comparison giving maximum similarity of base sequence when six extra bases have been added to the start of the sequence for a eukaryote organism. (b) Comparison between (1) Eukarya, (2) Archaea and (3) Bacteria. Bases in (2) and (3) that are the same as those in (1) are shaded red.

For decisions about what domain or kingdom an organism belongs to, molecular sequence data have been by far the most useful. However, such data are often less reliable for constructing phylogenies and classification at or below phylum level. We describe here one example which illustrates the conflict that may arise between morphological and molecular data: the relationship between whales and cattle.

Cattle belong to the mammalian order Artiodactyla, the even-toed hoofed mammals. For most of the 20th century this was regarded, from morphological data, as a classic monophyletic group (Figure 1.11a), with no specially close links to any other order. By the early 1990s, new morphological and molecular data indicated that artiodactyls and the order Cetacea (whales, porpoises and dolphins) shared a common ancestor, as illustrated in Figure 1.11b. In 1997, however, strong and apparently incontrovertible molecular evidence indicated that the situation is as shown in Figure 1.11c. The nature of this molecular evidence differs in detail from that described in Box 1.1 and, for interest only (you are not expected to remember it), is described in Box 1.2. This radical regrouping suggests that cows are more closely related to whales than to horses or even to pigs. Yet whales and their known fossil ancestors lack all the morphological characters regarded as diagnostic of artiodactyls (a characteristic heel joint, for example) so that, if Figure 1.11c is correct (and not all taxonomists think it is), cetaceans have undergone striking **divergent evolution** from their nearest relatives. The general message is that there is nothing immutable about higher taxa and you should expect many more changes of the kind just described as better molecular data become available. Higher taxa represent hypotheses that need to be altered as new evidence comes to light. Do bear this point in mind as you study domains, kingdoms and phylogenies in the following sections.

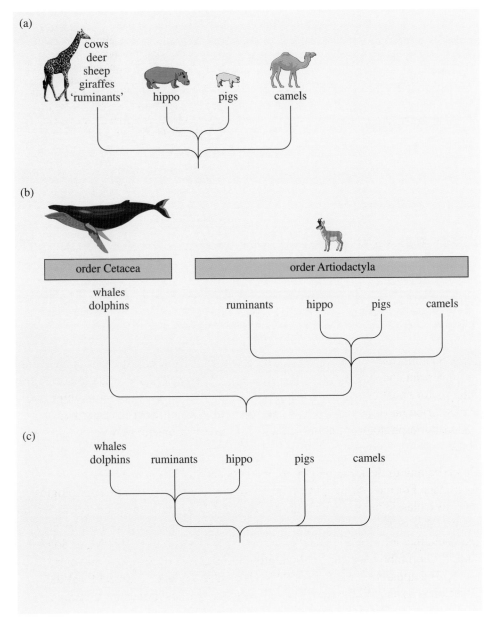

Figure 1.11 The changing phylogeny of the Artiodactyla. (a) Classic view of the order based solely on morphological evidence. (b) View in the early 1990s, with close links to the order Cetacea, based on morphological and molecular evidence. (c) View based on the molecular data of Shimamura *et al.* (1997).

BOX 1.2   MOLECULAR EVIDENCE LINKING WHALES AND ARTIODACTYLS

The evidence used depends on identifying *molecular markers* called SINEs (meaning short interspersed elements) which are inserted into nuclear DNA. SINEs comprise from one to a few hundred base pairs and are recognized because they have the same base sequence as a known RNA molecule (e.g. a transfer RNA): the RNA is reverse transcribed (i.e. copied as a DNA molecule, with the base thymine replacing uracil) and the transcript, or some part of it, is inserted into DNA.

The consensus view is that SINEs are only ever inserted once at a particular site (locus) on DNA and are never precisely excised. So if two groups have the same SINE at the same site, they must, by this argument, share a common ancestor. Figure 1.12 shows the occurrence of nine SINEs (a–i) discovered by Shimamura *et al.* (1997), all at different loci, within the artiodactyls and Cetacea. None occurred in the pig or camel lines of descent (lineages) but three (a, b, c) were found in all species examined from the Cetacea, hippopotamus and ruminant lineages. This is regarded as incontrovertible evidence that these three lineages form a monophyletic group. The remaining six SINEs were distributed as shown in Figure 1.12, two being unique to the cetacean lineage (d, e) and two to the ruminant lineage (f, g).

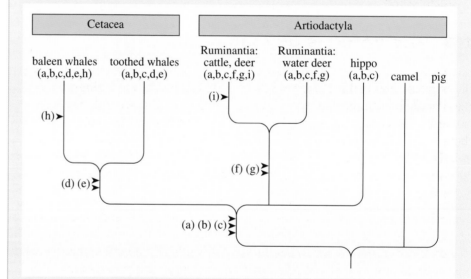

Figure 1.12   Phylogenetic relationships among cetaceans and artiodactyls as deduced from the sites of insertion of SINEs (a–i). Arrows indicate the timing of SINE insertion, so that all lineages beyond an arrow contain that SINE.

SUMMARY OF SECTION 1.2

1   Most taxonomists aim to classify organisms in a natural way that reflects the common origin of any named group from a single common ancestor and can be used to construct family trees or phylogenies which reflect evolutionary relationships.

2   Species are the smallest taxa to be universally recognized and are given a unique, Latin binomial name. Their biological definition relates to the capacity to interbreed to produce fertile offspring.

3   The biological species definition is often impossible to apply because breeding tests cannot be carried out. Hence structural and other characteristics are commonly used to delimit species. Among the problems that arise are: (a) identical appearance of species, sometimes as a result of convergent evolution; (b) disagreements among taxonomists (splitters and lumpers); (c) lack of structural markers in prokaryotes, and (d) gene transfer between species.

4   The taxonomic hierarchy groups organisms into progressively larger units: genus, family, order, class, phylum (or division), kingdom and domain. Each unit should be monophyletic. The higher the taxonomic category shared by two organisms, the further back in time is their common ancestor.

5   Characters that are used to estimate relatedness for higher taxonomic units should reflect deep, underlying similarities (homologies) of structure or physiology or molecules and avoid superficial similarities that have arisen through convergent evolution. Fossil evidence provides the best method of determining the time at which groups diverged in the past but is unavailable for many groups. Molecular sequence comparisons are increasingly used to delimit higher taxonomic groups and determine their evolutionary relationships.

1.3   THE DOMAINS OF LIFE

Having considered how organisms are classified, we can begin to examine the larger groups and in this section we discuss the largest units of biological classification, the three domains: **Bacteria** (sometimes Eubacteria), **Archaea** (sometimes Archaebacteria) and **Eukarya**. The first living cells evolved on Earth about 4 000 million years (Ma) ago and it is thought that the domains diverged (relatively) shortly afterwards, so their common ancestor would have been among the earliest organisms on Earth. The differences between domains reflect the beginnings of biological diversity.

Bacteria and Archaea actually *look* very similar (Figure 1.13) and the common name used for both is bacteria. Both are at the **prokaryotic** grade of organization, so they lack a nucleus or any other type of membrane-bound cell organelle, and a typical bacterium or archaeon (the name given to a member of the Archaea) is a single-celled microbe. Eukarya, however, have evolved into a huge diversity of different forms, many of them multicellular and including all animals and plants. Once again the structure or **morphology** of organisms — what you can see — is a poor guide to relatedness.

The differences between domains relate to fundamental features of cell composition and organization. Yet Archaea were not recognized as a separate group until the early 1980s, when molecular sequence analysis (as described in Box 1.1 and using the gene for an rRNA) showed that living organisms fell into three distinct groups. Only after this discovery were differences between Archaea and the other domains sought — and found. You will learn more about these differences after studying cell structure and biochemistry, but a few examples are listed overleaf:

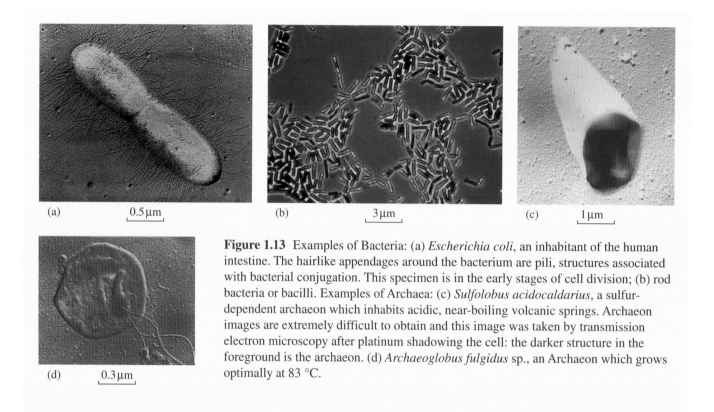

(a) 0.5 μm   (b) 3 μm   (c) 1 μm

(d) 0.3 μm

Figure 1.13 Examples of Bacteria: (a) *Escherichia coli*, an inhabitant of the human intestine. The hairlike appendages around the bacterium are pili, structures associated with bacterial conjugation. This specimen is in the early stages of cell division; (b) rod bacteria or bacilli. Examples of Archaea: (c) *Sulfolobus acidocaldarius*, a sulfur-dependent archaeon which inhabits acidic, near-boiling volcanic springs. Archaeon images are extremely difficult to obtain and this image was taken by transmission electron microscopy after platinum shadowing the cell: the darker structure in the foreground is the archaeon. (d) *Archaeoglobus fulgidus* sp., an Archaeon which grows optimally at 83 °C.

- Only Eukarya attain the eukaryotic grade of organization and have a membrane-bound nucleus and organelles such as mitochondria and chloroplasts.

- Archaea have uniquely structured membrane lipids (with a distinctive type of linkage between fatty acids and their anchoring stem) found in no other organism.

- The genetic material (DNA) of Archaea and Bacteria is *usually* organized as a single, circular chromosome but as several linear chromosomes in Eukarya. Only Eukarya commonly have histone proteins associated with DNA; Archaea sometimes contain histones, but Bacteria never do.

- There are differences in the machinery for protein synthesis (e.g. size and shape of ribosomes and sensitivity to certain inhibitors).

At this stage you are not expected to remember these differences but you should be able to appreciate what is meant by 'fundamental differences of cell structure and molecular organization'.

Figure 1.14 shows two possible phylogenies of the three domains based on molecular sequence data.

○ Which domain is more closely related to Eukarya according to Figure 1.14a?

● The Archaea: the rRNA sequence data suggest that there was first a separation of Bacteria and Archaea and then Eukarya evolved from an Archaea-like ancestor.

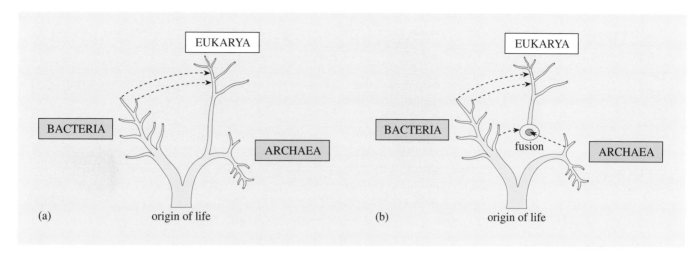

Figure 1.14 A phylogeny of the three domains based on (a) rRNA sequence data; (b) molecular sequence data from various proteins.

Figure 1.14a represents the orthodox view about the origin of Eukarya. You met this idea, which we shall refer to as the **Archaea hypothesis**, in Box 1.1. Figure 1.14b illustrates an alternative hypothesis which is supported mainly by sequence comparisons of certain proteins which, like rRNA, appear to have changed very little over evolutionary time. The alternative or **fusion hypothesis** suggests that eukaryotic cells arose initially by a *fusion* between a bacterium and an archaeon. Figure 1.15 shows one version of what might have happened.

However the Eukarya arose — and it is still too early to say which of the Archaea and the fusion hypotheses is nearer the truth — the first eukaryotic cells are usually assumed to have had a flexible outer surface (i.e. lacking a rigid outer wall), a nucleus, and to have lived as **heterotrophs** (meaning 'other-feeding') by feeding on living or dead organic matter. It is even possible that these cells were **chemoautotrophs**, that is, they obtained energy by oxidizing simple inorganic molecules. Like all organisms on the early Earth, however, the first Eukarya did not use oxygen (O_2) for respiration because there *was* no free O_2 in the atmosphere. By 3500 Ma ago, however, a photosynthetic pathway had evolved in one group of Bacteria (the Cyanobacteria) which released oxygen from water and this process of **oxygenic photosynthesis** led very gradually to a build-up of free O_2. As aerobic habitats appeared, groups of heterotrophic bacteria evolved the capacity to use O_2 to oxidize food molecules in cell respiration, thus releasing much more energy than other, anaerobic forms of respiration. The Eukarya were left behind in this metabolic race, evolving neither photosynthesis nor aerobic metabolism, but the dashed lines in Figure 1.14a indicate how they acquired these properties.

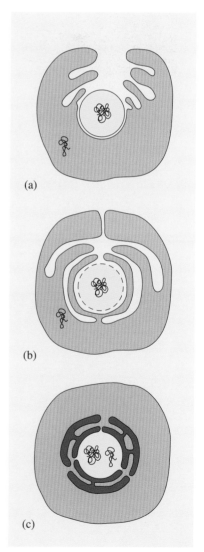

Figure 1.15 Origin of the eukaryotic cell and the nucleus according to one version of the fusion hypothesis. (a) A bacterial cell with a flexible surface (the host) engulfed an archaeon cell (the smaller partner or symbiont). (b) The archaeon cell was surrounded by folds of the host's outer membrane and lost its own outer membrane.
(c) Bacterial DNA transferred to the archaeon which became the nucleus of the cell (the ancestral eukaryotic cell). The nucleus was surrounded by a double membrane with links to other internal membranes, all derived from the infolded membranes shown in (b).

○ What do the dashed lines indicate?

● They indicate that cells from Bacteria were engulfed and incorporated within cells of Eukarya, where they eventually lost their independence. Much of their DNA was transferred to the host nucleus and they became distinct cell organelles performing specialized functions.

The name given to this incorporation process is **endosymbiosis** (from the Greek words for 'inside', endo, and 'living together', symbiosis). The first endosymbiotic event gave rise to the organelles called **mitochondria**. Mitochondria gave Eukarya the capacity for aerobic metabolism and this opened up aerobic habitats for colonization. The significance of this event for eukaryotic diversification is discussed further in Chapter 2. The other endosymbiotic event shown in Figure 1.14 is that which gave rise to **chloroplasts**, the organelles that use light as a source of energy and carry out the process of photosynthesis. This step allowed some Eukarya to switch from heterotrophy to **autotrophy**, that is, 'self-feeding', and able to use simple carbon compounds such as carbon dioxide gas (CO_2) as a source of carbon, and light as a source of energy. Just as gene transfer between prokaryotes (Section 1.2.1) allowed transfer of one or a few genes to distantly related species, so endosymbiosis allowed transfer of complete genomes to unrelated organisms. Transformation of the endosymbiont into a dependent organelle involved further gene transfer — from prokaryote DNA to the host nucleus — which underlines further the evolutionary significance of gene transfer.

Possession of mitochondria and/or chloroplasts is one of the distinguishing features of modern Eukarya and it contributed enormously to their diversification. This diversification has resulted mainly from changes in cell structure, the arrangements of cells in multicellular organisms and the formation of complex associations between organisms. An overview of eukaryotic diversity is given in Section 1.5. In the Archaea and Bacteria, however, metabolic rather than structural diversity has dominated and you have already seen that both oxygenic (O_2-releasing) photosynthesis and aerobic metabolism evolved first in Bacteria. Prokaryotes are vital for sustaining life on this planet and the next Section outlines the main types of Archaea and Bacteria.

SUMMARY OF SECTION 1.3

1 The deepest division of living organisms (the highest taxonomic grouping) is into three domains: Bacteria, Archaea and Eukarya. These domains separated from a universal common ancestor shortly after the origin of life, about 4000 Ma ago.

2 Domains and, in particular, the existence of Archaea were first recognized on the basis of molecular sequence comparisons of a gene for rRNA. Other distinguishing characteristics relate to cell structure, chemical linkages in membrane lipids, packaging of DNA and the protein synthesis machinery.

3   Bacteria and Archaea are prokaryotes (lacking membrane-bound organelles) whereas Eukarya attain a higher grade of organization with membrane-bound organelles, that is, a nucleus and, usually, mitochondria and/or chloroplasts. The first eukaryotic cells may have evolved from the Archaea (the Archaea hypothesis) or may have arisen through a fusion between a bacterial and an archaeon cell (the fusion hypothesis). Mitochondria and chloroplasts were obtained later from Bacteria, by endosymbiosis.

1.4 THE PROKARYOTIC KINGDOMS

Having considered the most fundamental division of living organisms into three domains, we turn now to the next level of diversification, the kingdoms. The main purpose of this and the next section is to define the kingdoms and indicate the sorts of organism they contain.

Figure 1.16 shows a simplified separation of the three domains (blue, pink and white) into seven kingdoms (balloons), and the greater diversity of Eukarya, which has four of the kingdoms, is clear. However, this lack of diversity in the Archaea and Bacteria is an illusion that stems mainly from the great difficulties in classifying these organisms (Section 1.2.1) and disagreements about the degree of difference that is necessary to recognize a separate kingdom. With the advent of molecular sequencing techniques there has been a revolution in prokaryote taxonomy, with major new groupings being recognized within domains and new family trees beginning to take shape. The revolution is ongoing and still far from complete so that the classification described here is likely to change in the future.

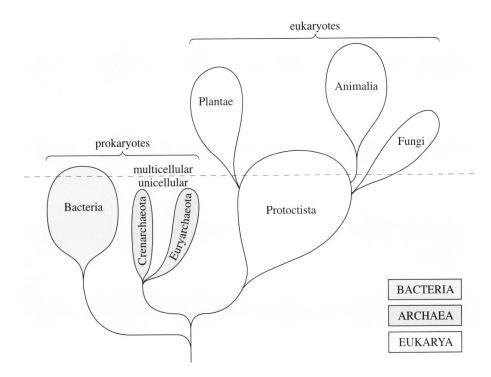

Figure 1.16 A simplified phylogeny showing the separation of the three domains into seven kingdoms.

1.4.1 THE ARCHAEAN KINGDOMS

New archaeons are discovered every year but, so far, all are structurally simple although often irregular in shape, for example, small ovoid cells (cocci), short rods or longer filaments. Some examples of archaeons are shown in Figure 1.17.

Figure 1.17 Some examples of archaeons. (a) *Methanobacterium ruminantum*: drawing of a cross-section of a methanogenic bacterium taken from a cow rumen. The bacterium has nearly finished dividing and a new cell wall is almost complete.
(b) *Thermoplasma acidophilum*: drawing to show the lobular structure typical of this organism which lacks a cell wall.

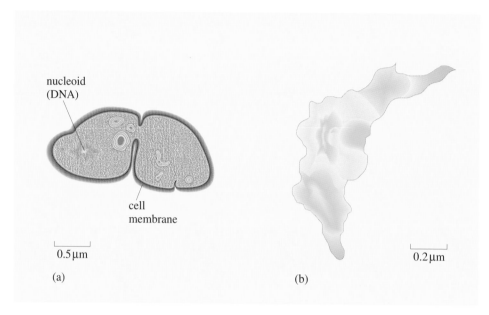

nucleoid (DNA)

cell membrane

0.5 μm

(a)

0.2 μm

(b)

The striking thing about archaeons is their metabolic diversity and, in particular, the extraordinary range of extreme habitats in which they occur: hot volcanic springs, deep-sea hydrothermal vents, acid mine wastes, the Dead Sea and the rumens of cattle, to name just a few. Habitat preference and metabolism are reflected to some extent in classification, see Figure 1.18. The kingdom **Crenarchaeota**, which contains the oldest lineages (*cren* comes from the Greek word for 'spring' or 'source'), has genera that depend on sulfur in various ways and often require very hot conditions (85–100 °C). Names such as *Thermoproteus* and *Sulfolobus* reflect the thermophilic (heat-loving) and sulfur-dependent nature of the organisms. *Sulfolobus*, for example, inhabits acidic, near-boiling and sulfur-rich volcanic springs. Nevertheless, it is the distinctive nature of their rRNA which primarily defines the Crenarchaeota and during the 1990s three new groups of crenarchaeotes were discovered, widely distributed in the open ocean and in lake and marsh sediments at normal temperatures.

The kingdom **Euryarchaeota** is, metabolically speaking, more of a mixed bag (*eury* is Greek for 'broad' or 'general'). Extreme halophiles (salt-lovers) live in places such as the Dead Sea, salt pans, brines and even salted foods, where the concentration of salt is higher than in normal seawater. One member of this group has evolved a unique way of trapping light energy using a purple pigment in the outer membrane. The other group, **methanogens,** produce methane (CH_4, marsh gas), which is the main component of natural gas. They are widespread in anaerobic (oxygen-free) environments such as waterlogged soil, marshes, sediments and the fermenting chamber, or rumen, of ruminants such as cattle.

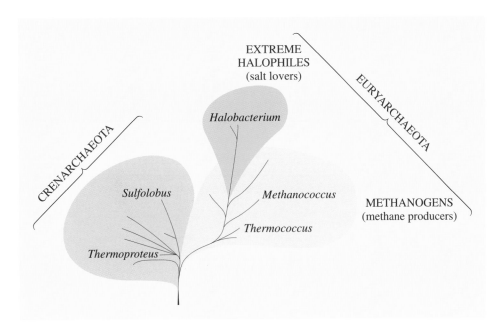

Figure 1.18 The archaean kingdoms. A third kingdom, Korarchaeota, basal to the other two kingdoms, is sometimes distinguished.

It appears, therefore, that archaeons from both kingdoms are largely restricted to exotic or extreme habitats. There are strong indications, however, that this conclusion is unsafe and could be the result of the way Archaea were studied. In the past, for example, microbiologists were intrigued to discover microbes living in strange places, isolated them and subsequently, through rRNA analysis, classified them as archaeons. People rarely looked for archaeons in 'normal' habitats. Now, however, using archaeon rRNA sequences as *probes* (which bind specifically to any complementary RNA or DNA), a wider search is being undertaken, and people are finding archaeons in ordinary seawater, the normal-temperature strains of crenarchaeotes mentioned earlier being one example. In all probability, archaeons are far more widespread than they appeared to be.

1.4.2 THE KINGDOM BACTERIA

In terms of their metabolism, Bacteria are even more diverse than Archaea and certainly show much greater structural diversity. So the fact that there is currently only one kingdom in this domain reflects history, not uniformity, and the classification may well change in the future. One suggestion is that many of the groups currently classed as phyla will be reclassed as kingdoms. Figure 1.19 shows the main phyla within bacteria, based on rRNA sequence analysis; you will meet many of the phyla again and, at this stage, are *not* expected to remember this classification but to use it as a source of reference. In Figure 1.19, for most phyla, only common names are given or else the name of a characteristic genus. The name of Gram-positive bacteria refers to their positive response to the Gram stain.

Figure 1.19 A family tree, based on rRNA sequence analysis, showing the classification into phyla within the domain and kingdom Bacteria. Phyla shown in green include members able to carry out photosynthesis.

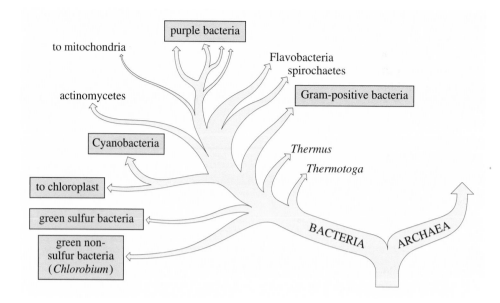

○ From the names alone, what similarity can you see between two of the lower branches on the bacterial family tree and the Crenarchaeota?

● 'Therm' appears in the names of genera characterizing two of the lower branches, indicating a link with *heat* (*therma*). These bacteria are indeed thermophilic (heat-loving), a property characteristic of many extant crenarchaeotes (Section 1.4.1). It is thought that life might have originated in hot environments and thermophily in the most ancient microbial lineages could reflect this origin.

Two other points to notice in Figure 1.19 are:

1 The ability to use light as a source of energy in photosynthesis — photo-autotrophy, shown as green shading — appears in five separate lineages (although only the Cyanobacteria release O_2 during photosynthesis). This could mean *either* that photosynthesis evolved separately five times, *or* that some primitive photosynthetic system was present in early bacteria on the trunk of the family tree and five specialist lines evolved from it. The latter solution is currently favoured but the question is still not resolved.

2 The *purple bacteria* (also called the Proteobacteria, and some of which are purple-red in colour) with their four sub-branches at the tip of the tree form the largest and most diverse bacterial phylum. Its members range from *E. coli* (a much-studied bacterium that is common in mammalian guts), to nitrifying bacteria (soil or water dwellers whose activity leads to the formation of nitrate from ammonia), to photosynthetic species; until the rRNA family tree was developed, all these species were placed in different phyla. Note also that mitochondria (top left) originated from this group.

The above discussion just hints at the metabolic range of the bacteria, which is truly extraordinary: they can obtain energy in more ways than found in any other kingdom, break down almost all organic compounds and live almost everywhere (although not specializing in the extreme habitats favoured by Archaea). Part of the reason for this diversity is *gene transfer* (Section 1.2.1). There is good evidence that the ability to 'fix' nitrogen gas (convert N_2 into NH_3), to synthesize antibiotics and other complex secondary products, and to invade particular host species have all been spread within and between bacterial phyla (and even to other kingdoms) by gene transfer. When the complete genome (DNA) of the Gram-positive bacterium *Bacillus subtilis* was sequenced in 1997, at least nine sites were identified where genes had been transferred by bacterial viruses. So gene transfer is an ancient and important evolutionary process and it is also the basis of modern genetic engineering.

Structural complexity in the Bacteria extends well beyond the simple and very small cocci, rods and filaments that are typical of Archaea. Several phyla include species that are truly **multicellular**, that is, comprise different types of cells that perform different functions for the whole individual. Some cyanobacteria form chains of cells that include cells specialized to 'fix' nitrogen (Figure 1.20). The actinomycetes (phylum Actinomycota) commonly form branched, multicellular filaments that spread over a substrate and then send up aerial branches which produce and release single-celled, resistant spores (Figure 1.21). The majority of fungi (a eukaryotic kingdom, Figure 1.16) have a remarkably similar growth form and many also produce spores for dispersal in a similar way. For this reason 'mycete' or 'mycota', meaning 'fungal', appears in the name of the bacterial phylum. But actinomycetes and fungi are *not* closely related: their similarities do not reflect descent from a common ancestor, but have arisen independently through the process of *convergent evolution* (Section 1.2.1) — these represent one of the best examples of this process and are worth remembering.

Figure 1.20 Examples of Bacteria. (a) Part of a filament of the cyanobacterium *Anabaena* sp. showing a specialized cell (heterocyst) which fixes nitrogen and a spore cell. (b) Light micrograph of unattached spirochaete, *Spirochaeta plicatilis*. (c) Electron micrograph of a single *Vibrio cholerae*. The single large hairlike flagellum is used for movement.

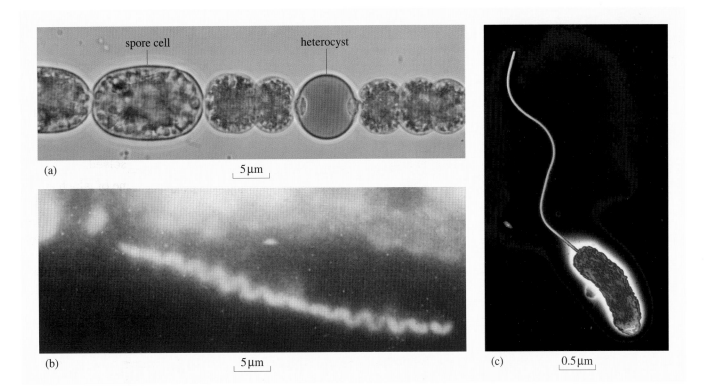

Figure 1.21 The multicellular filaments or hyphae of an actinomycete *Streptomyces* sp. showing spores at the tips of erect (aerial) hyphae.

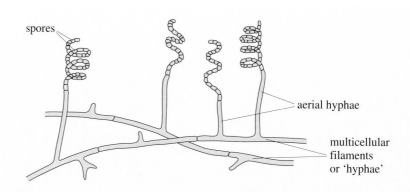

spores

aerial hyphae

multicellular filaments or 'hyphae'

8 μm

Figure 1.22 Large spirochaetes *Pillotina sp.*, from the gut of an American wood-eating termite.

100 μm

Figure 1.23 The largest known bacterium, *Epulopiscium fishelsoni*, from the gut of a Red Sea surgeonfish.

Finally, on the question of *cell size*, bacterial cells are usually small — 1 to 5 μm long — but there are many exceptions. Among the spirochaetes (Figure 1.20d), which have a characteristic shape like a coiled spring, there are some which are up to 3 μm wide and over 100 μm long (Figure 1.22). These giant spirochaetes all live symbiotically within invertebrate animals, notably in the guts of wood-eating termites, but even they are dwarfed by Gram-positive bacteria in the guts of surgeonfish from warm-water reefs. These monsters can measure 80×600 μm (Figure 1.23) and when first discovered were thought to be protoctists, that is, eukaryotes.

○ (a) How, *using a microscope*, could you determine that these organisms were prokaryotes and not eukaryotes?

(b) How, *using a molecular technique* described earlier, could their identity as Bacteria rather than Archaea be established?

● (a) Absence of a nucleus surrounded by a nuclear membrane, which is characteristic of prokaryotes, should be clear in a light or electron microscope.

(b) Base sequences of genes for ribosomal RNA should distinguish Bacteria from Archaea and might also allow classification to phylum level.

rRNA sequence comparisons were used to establish the nature of these bacteria, yet another example of the usefulness of this technique.

SUMMARY OF SECTION 1.4

1 The degree of difference necessary to separate organisms into kingdoms is still disputed and so, therefore, is the number of kingdoms. Here we recognize seven kingdoms, three prokaryotic and four eukaryotic. More prokaryotic kingdoms are likely to be recognized in the future as further molecular sequence data are obtained.

2 In the prokaryote domain Archaea, two kingdoms are usually recognized on the basis of rRNA sequence comparisons: Crenarchaeota and Euryarchaeota. The most ancient lineages occur within the Crenarchaeota and include microbes that live in hot, acid conditions (such as volcanic springs) and have a sulfur-dependent metabolism. Euryarchaeota include extreme halophiles

and methanogens (methane producers). All archaeons appear to be structurally simple unicells and, although the majority of known species occur in extreme habitats, the use of archaeon rRNA probes is revealing their widespread occurrence (especially of crenarchaeotes) in normal habitats such as seawater.

3   The domain Bacteria with its single kingdom shows a greater range of structural and metabolic diversity than the Archaea. As in the Archaea, some of the oldest lineages are thermophilic. The ability to use light energy (photo-autotrophy), multicellularity and spore production have evolved in several lineages. Some unicellular species from animal guts can be very large. Gene transfer is probably responsible for much of the metabolic diversity in bacteria.

1.5   THE EUKARYOTIC KINGDOMS

In Figure 1.16 — and in most elementary textbooks — four eukaryotic kingdoms are shown. However, the taxonomic revolution brought about by molecular techniques has now spread from prokaryotes to eukaryotes and, although Protoctista is the kingdom whose classification has been most affected, all eukaryotic kingdoms have undergone drastic taxonomic revision in the 1980s and 90s. We have tried to present a 'consensus' version of eukaryote phylogeny, taxonomy and nomenclature here, but be aware that many other versions exist; the one thing you can be sure of is that these modern versions differ considerably from anything you might find in older textbooks.

1.5.1   PROTOCTISTA, THE 'DUSTBIN KINGDOM'

The branches that emerge low down on the eukaryote family tree have conventionally been grouped together as one huge, heterogeneous kingdom, the **Protoctista**. Even the name Protoctista is disputed. Originally this kingdom was called Protozoa, meaning 'first animals', but many members are plant-like autotrophs and so the name Protista ('first organisms') was adopted, which avoided commitment to any particular type of feeding but implied that organisms were all single-celled. However, some lineages include large *multicellular* forms (including brown and red seaweeds of sea-shores) so the name Protoctista ('first to be established') was proposed. All three of these names are still widely used.

Defining Protoctista is not easy but, broadly, they are *all the unicellular eukaryotes and any multicellular descendants that are neither plants, animals nor fungi* (all of which we define later). In short, any eukaryote that is not an animal, plant or fungus is a protoctist, hence the epithet 'dustbin kingdom'. Apart from the large seaweeds, the majority of protoctists are not visible without using a microscope, so they are probably not familiar to you. Yet the oceans, soil and freshwaters teem with these organisms and their importance as primary producers and components of food webs is inestimable.

There is huge diversity of species, structure and mode of life but a characteristic found in most protoctistans for at least one stage in their life cycle is possession of one or more **flagella** (singular, flagellum). Small flagella, usually occurring in large numbers, are referred to as **cilia** (singular, cilium). Figure 1.24 illustrates a simple flagellate and a ciliate. These whip-like, motile structures perform a variety of functions in locomotion and feeding (discussed further in Chapter 2), but one point to emphasize is that they are *not* descended from or homologous to the bacterial flagella (Figure 1.20) and are unique to eukaryotes: their structure, molecular composition, and even the mechanism causing them to move are quite different.

Figure 1.24 (a) A protoctist flagellate, *Bodo* sp., a kinetoplastid; (b) a ciliate, *Paramecium* sp.

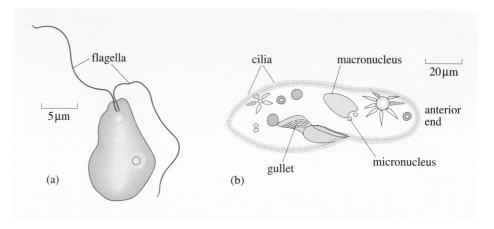

Many protoctist lineages are as different from each other as animals are from plants and so, logically, they should be regarded as separate kingdoms. Until the 1990s, however, too little was known about protoctistan relationships to re-group them in any sensible and widely acceptable way. This re-grouping is now underway, supported by rRNA comparisons, although there is still much disagreement and debate and some taxonomists divide the protoctists into three or more kingdoms. Figure 1.25 shows one version which you are *not* expected to memorize but rather to use as a source of reference and a guide when using the *GLO* CD-ROM. You will learn more about protoctistan classification in Chapter 2.

The different coloured boxes and circles in Figure 1.25 indicate the sorts of biologists who studied (and named) that group. Green or partially green boxes include '**algae**', which simply means any protoctists having chloroplasts; they were studied by botanists. The blue boxes were regarded as fungi and studied by mycologists. And the remainder, white boxes, include heterotrophs and were studied by zoologists. Botanical names of phyla (or divisions) commonly end in 'phyta', mycological names end in 'mycota' or 'mycete' and zoological names end in a variety of ways but include 'zoa' (animals) and 'poda' (feet). It is partly because the study of protoctists has been split between different groups of biologists, working separately and communicating infrequently, that protoctistan classification has been so confused.

Despite its complexity, Figure 1.25 does not include all recognized protoctistan phyla. We discuss diversity among protoctists in more detail in Chapter 2 and, at the end of this chapter, you can see what some of the protoctistan groups actually look like by using the *GLO* CD-ROM. However, three points are worth noting here.

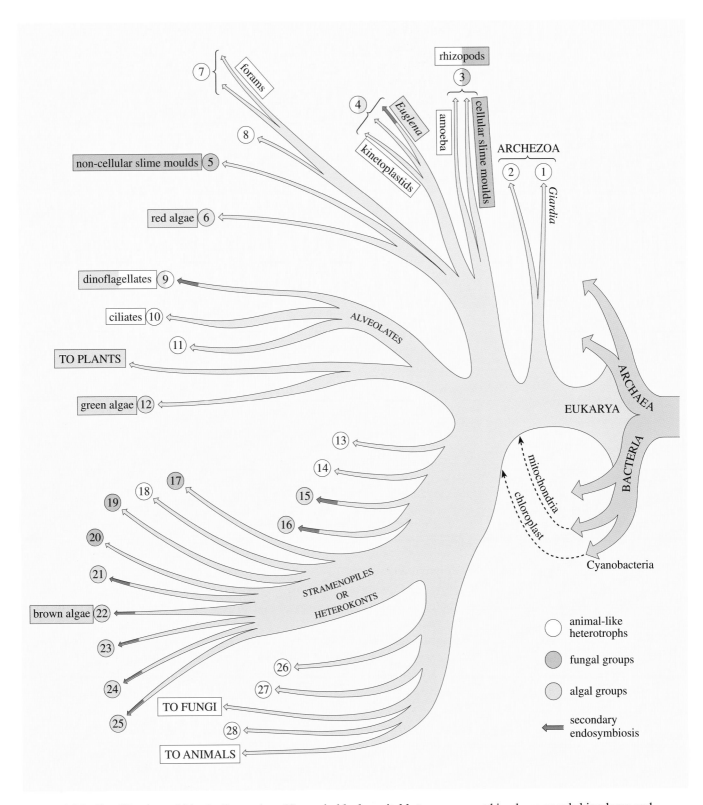

Figure 1.25 Classification within the Protoctista. Names in black capital letters represent kingdoms or sub-kingdoms and names in small capital letters represent superphyla. Dashed lines indicate primary endosymbiotic events (the origins of mitochondria and chloroplasts). Red-tipped arrows indicate secondary endosymbiosis where chloroplasts were acquired from a eukaryotic alga. Names in lower-case letters are examples of common names and phyla. The numbers in coloured circles represent the different phyla and are listed in Chapter 2.

(i) The Archezoa

The lowest branches on the tree, that is, the oldest lineages, are sometimes classified as a separate kingdom, the **Archezoa** (meaning 'ancient animals') and are here treated as a subkingdom.

○ From Figure 1.25, how do the Archezoa differ from other protoctistans?

● They lack mitochondria. As shown in the figure, the endosymbiotic event that gave rise to mitochondria is thought to have occurred after these groups separated from the main eukaryote line.

Because they lack mitochondria, Archezoa cannot carry out aerobic respiration and all live in environments where there is little or no oxygen. Such habitats include the guts of vertebrates and many Archezoa are parasites: *Giardia lamblia,* for example (Figure 1.26), occurs in human intestines and causes a serious diarrhoeal disease, giardiasis. Archezoa have several other features which are regarded as 'primitive'. They lack peroxisomes (a cell organelle that contains powerful detoxifying enzymes able to produce and break down hydrogen peroxide), have only a very simple system of internal membranes, and *Giardia* has an rRNA which is much more like that of Bacteria than is that of any other eukaryote.

Archezoans have become a focus of research because their study might shed light on the nature of the earliest eukaryotic cells.

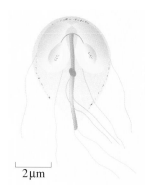

2 μm

Figure 1.26 *Giardia lamblia*, an archezoan protoctist that lives in the human gut and causes the disease giardiasis.

(ii) Endosymbiosis and chloroplasts

The endosymbiotic *acquisition of mitochondria* and, later, *chloroplasts* were the two events that really opened up the world to protoctists, allowing them to exploit a far greater range of habitats; we discuss this further in Chapter 2. In particular, the mass of branches radiating at the crown of the protoctistan family tree (Figure 1.25) is thought to depend strongly on chloroplast acquisition. However, notice all the red arrow heads in Figure 1.25. They indicate that chloroplasts were acquired not from a cyanobacterium (an evolutionary step which probably happened *only once,* **primary endosymbiosis**), but from another *eukaryote* by a process of **secondary endosymbiosis**. Figure 1.27 illustrates how primary endosymbiosis is thought to have occurred, the end-product being a chloroplast surrounded by two membranes. Figure 1.28 shows various stages in secondary endosymbiosis, the end-products being chloroplasts surrounded by three or four membranes.

○ From Figure 1.28, describe the origin of the four outer membranes seen in a type 1 chloroplast, as found in cryptophyte algae and some dinoflagellates.

● The outermost membrane derives from the food vacuole membrane of the original eukaryotic host; the next membrane derives from the plasma membrane of the algal endosymbiont; and the two inner membranes are the chloroplast membranes of the primary chloroplast in the algal endosymbiont. Notice that a remnant of the endosymbiont nucleus may persist as a structure called the *nucleomorph* or *cryptonucleus*. Type 2 chloroplasts also have four membranes but the outermost one differs from that of type 1 (see Figure 1.28).

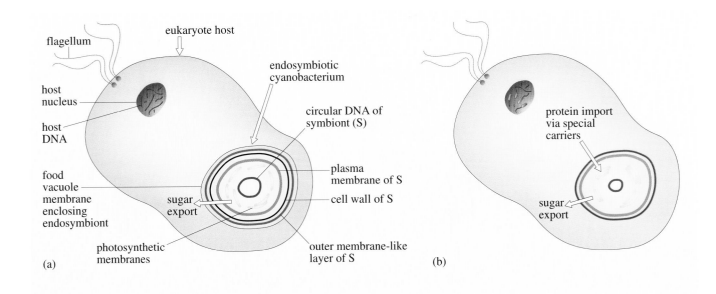

Figure 1.27 Primary endosymbiosis. (a) Initial state with a cyanobacterium present as an endosymbiont (S) in a heterotrophic eukaryote host cell. (b) The same host cell with a fully integrated chloroplast that has two outer membranes. Note that some genetic material has been transferred from the chloroplast to the host nucleus.

○ What happened to produce the type 3 chloroplast (with three surrounding membranes) shown in Figure 1.28? Check your answer and then write it in the box marked X on the figure.

● The outermost membrane, which was that of the food vacuole in the original host, has been completely lost.

Only two algal phyla have chloroplasts derived by primary endosymbiosis: the green algae (Chlorophyta, phylum 12) and the red algae (Rhodophyta, phylum 6), neither of which is labelled with a red arrow head in Figure 1.25. Comparisons of rRNA genes in chloroplasts of these two types of algae suggest that the chloroplasts have evolved from the *same* cyanobacterial ancestor, which is why primary endosymbiosis is thought to have occurred only once. Sorting out who donated chloroplasts to whom in secondary endosymbiosis has been more difficult, but careful comparisons of chloroplast pigments and rRNA gene sequences have provided many of the answers. For example, the nucleomorph of cryptophyte algae (Figure 1.28, type 1) carries the unmistakable signature of the red algae; so cryptophytes originated when a heterotrophic host eukaryote took on board a red algal endosymbiont.

Secondary endosymbiosis, involving two eukaryotes, occurred many times and, equally, *loss* of photosynthetic capacity, by losing chloroplasts or the pigment chlorophyll, has occurred in several protoctist lineages. Such gains and losses of chloroplasts have contributed greatly to diversification in protoctists.

Figure 1.28 Secondary endosymbiosis: the acquisition of chloroplasts from a eukaryotic alga and subsequent evolution to produce different types of chloroplasts, 1, 2 and 3.

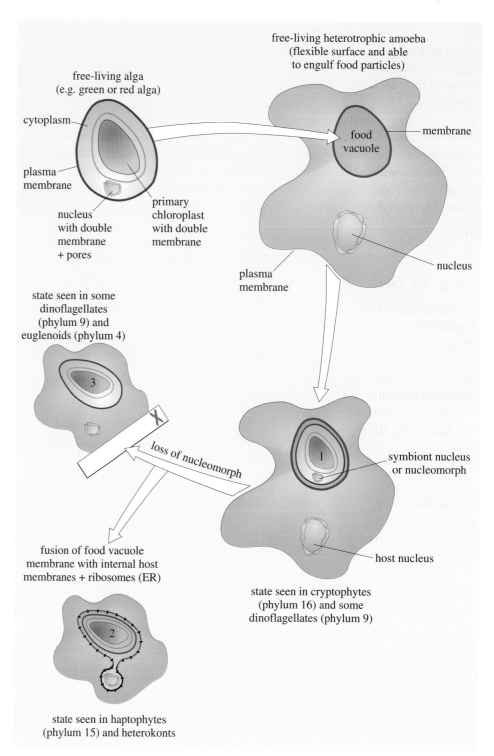

free-living heterotrophic amoeba (flexible surface and able to engulf food particles)

free-living alga (e.g. green or red alga)

cytoplasm

food vacuole

membrane

plasma membrane

nucleus with double membrane + pores

primary chloroplast with double membrane

plasma membrane

nucleus

state seen in some dinoflagellates (phylum 9) and euglenoids (phylum 4)

3

loss of nucleomorph

1

symbiont nucleus or nucleomorph

host nucleus

fusion of food vacuole membrane with internal host membranes + ribosomes (ER)

state seen in cryptophytes (phylum 16) and some dinoflagellates (phylum 9)

2

state seen in haptophytes (phylum 15) and heterokonts

(iii) Unusual cell division and lack of sexual reproduction

A final general point about protoctists, and one that is not apparent from Figure 1.25, is that processes you may think of as standard in eukaryotes are variable or do not occur at all in many protoctists. The outstanding examples are mitosis, meiosis and sexual reproduction. The archezoan *Pelomyxa*, a sort of giant amoeba, has nothing approaching 'classical' mitosis and its nuclei appear to divide in two much as bacterial cells do. Many other protoctist lineages have unusual versions of mitosis and, overall, it appears that this process evolved in many different ways during protoctist evolution. In about half the protoctist lineages there is no evidence that either meiosis or sexual reproduction (nuclear fusion plus meiosis) occurs at all.

Diversity in protoctists is considered further in Chapter 2 but at this stage you may like to look at examples of this kingdom on the *GLO* CD-ROM.

1.5.2 PLANTS: THE KINGDOM PLANTAE

You are probably familiar with the types of plants that characterize phyla in the kingdom Plantae — mosses, ferns, conifers, etc. Familiarity and low diversity at the higher taxonomic level (there are only 12 phyla) are the main reasons for considering plants first among the multicellular eukaryote kingdoms. The aims of this section are simply to describe the general characteristics of plants so that you know what a plant is, and to provide a phylogeny of the kingdom so that you know the relationships between phyla and can explore for yourself, using the *GLO* CD-ROM, diversity within phyla.

WHAT IS A PLANT?

The simplest definition of a plant is that it is a *multicellular, eukaryotic photosynthetic organism adapted primarily to life on land.* The last characteristic differentiates plants from algae, most of which are primarily aquatic. However, some algae live on land in protected or damp habitats, some bryophytes (e.g. mosses) are rather poorly adapted to terrestrial life, and some complex plants have become secondarily adapted to aquatic life (e.g. pondweeds). Some plants, indeed, have become secondarily *non*-photosynthetic (e.g. parasites such as broomrapes, *Orobanche* spp.): there are always exceptions to a general definition.

Another characteristic differentiates plants from algae unequivocally: at some stage in their life cycle plants develop from an **embryo**, a diploid multicellular structure (the cells having two sets of chromosomes) which receives nourishment and protection from a parent, usually by being enclosed in maternal tissues (Figure 1.29). Such a protected embryo is thought to have been a key factor in the successful colonization of land by plants and, accordingly, an alternative name for the kingdom is Embryophyta.

Most animals also develop from an embryo, although of a different type and without the protective maternal tissues that are found in plants. As in animals, the plant embryo develops from a **zygote** (a fertilized egg produced by the fusion of two haploid gametes) to become a multicellular diploid adult. But there is an important difference between the life cycles of animals and plants, as illustrated in Figure 1.30.

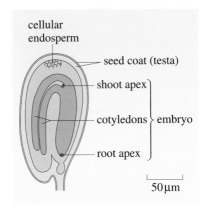

Figure 1.29 A partially developed embryo of a flowering plant (*Capsella bursa-pastoris*, shepherd's purse).

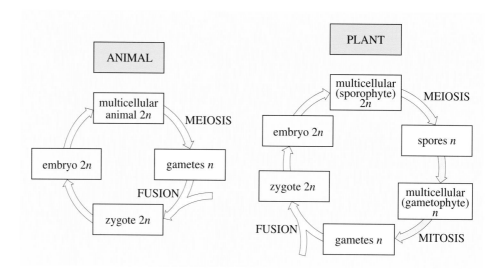

Figure 1.30 Comparison of plant and animal life cycles.

○ From the figure, describe three differences between plant and animal life cycles.

● (1) The plant life cycle has *two* multicellular stages, one haploid and the other diploid, whereas animals have only the diploid stage. (2) Meiosis in plants gives rise to *spores* (not gametes as in animals) and the multicellular haploid stage develops from a spore. (3) Gametes are the products of meiotic division in animals but of mitotic division (in the multicellular haploid stage) in plants.

The alternation of multicellular haploid and diploid stages in plants is termed **alternation of generations**. Although a similar alternation occurs in many algae (Chapter 2), it is regarded as a characteristic plant feature. The diploid, spore-producing generation is termed the **sporophyte** and the haploid, gamete-producing generation as the **gametophyte**.

Plants are non-motile and their cell structure differs from that in other multicellular kingdoms: mature cells usually have a central, fluid-filled *vacuole*; they contain *plastids* which, in green tissues, take the form of chloroplasts and in non-green tissues store food (e.g. starch or lipids); plant cells also have a rigid cell wall in which the polysaccharide *cellulose* plays a major structural role. Both paper and cotton are virtually pure, plant-derived cellulose, so the cellulosic walls of plants are very useful to humans.

We can now assemble a more complete definition of a plant. Typically, it

•   is a multicellular, eukaryotic autotroph that lives on land;

•   develops at some stage from an embryo;

- has an alternation of multicellular haploid and diploid generations, and
- is non-motile, having cells with a tough, cellulosic wall, a vacuole and plastids.

ORIGINS AND DIVERSIFICATION: PLANT PHYLOGENY

In evolutionary terms, plants are relatively recent, having originated about 500 Ma ago from green algal (Chlorophyta) ancestors that probably lived in freshwater. Because of the restrictions imposed by their mode of life — non-motile photosynthesizers — the range of form in plants is quite limited. First, there is a green, photosynthetic part which must be exposed to light and, in most plants, comprises an upright, branching structure, the **shoot**. Second, there are non-photosynthetic organs whose main functions are anchorage and absorption (e.g. of water and mineral ions). In later-evolved plants these structures are the **roots** but in other plants they may be modified shoots or simple hair-like processes called *rhizoids*. Shoots may become stiffened and woody and attain great heights, as in trees, but the basic form is still retained. The same applies even when plants have changed their mode of life and become partially or wholly heterotrophic, as in parasitic and insectivorous plants.

The diversification and classification of plants does not, therefore, relate primarily to overall structure (as it does in animals, Section 1.5.4) but rather to features of the life cycle, cell structure and the structures involved in reproduction and dispersal. Figure 1.31 (overleaf) shows one phylogeny and classification system for plants, based on fossil evidence and comparative studies, including molecular sequence comparisons. You are not expected to remember the Latin names of the 12 phyla (capital letters) but should try to learn the relationships between the broad groups (blue lines) and what is meant by the most widely used common names (bold black) so that you have some familiarity with the kingdom. The notes below are intended to help you do this but ideally you should link study of these notes and Figure 1.31 with the *GLO* CD-ROM, where you can see examples of all the main types of plants.

First, take a general look at Figure 1.31 and identify groups that show the greatest species diversity. **Flowering plants** or **angiosperms** (phylum Anthophyta), the most recently evolved group, clearly head the field, having more species than all other groups put together. Most of the plants you see, from oak trees to dandelions, belong to this group which dominates the land flora today.

○ Identify the next two most species-rich phyla.

● **Ferns** (Pterophyta), with 11 000 species and **mosses** (Bryophyta) with about 10 000 species.

Both of these groups are most abundant in the moist tropics and they occur mainly in habitats that are permanently or periodically damp.

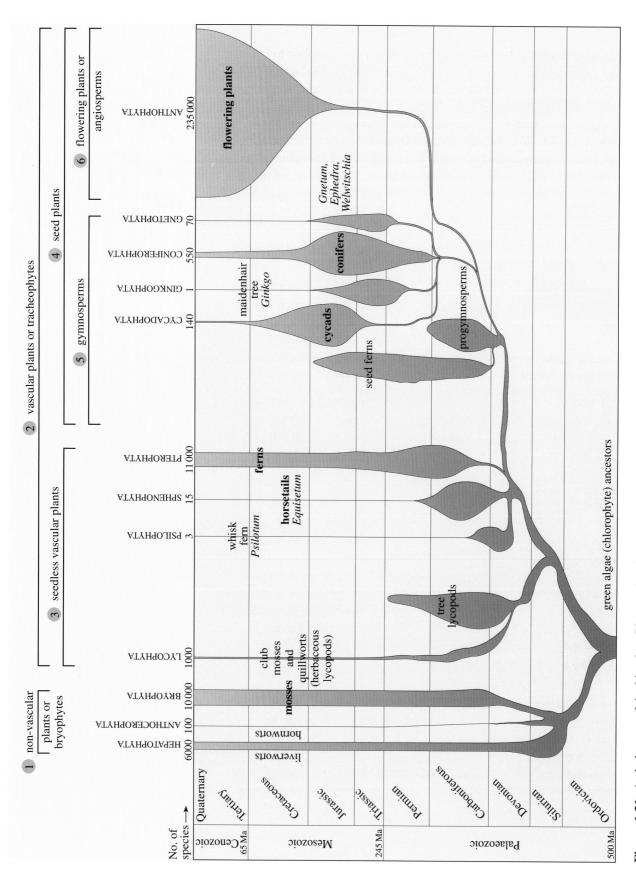

Figure 1.31 A phylogeny of the kingdom Plantae showing groups with living representatives or descendants. The vertical axis represents time and the width of different lineages indicates relative abundance. Names of phyla are shown in capital letters with numbers of living species given for each. Names in lower case print are either the common name for a phylum (e.g. ferns) or the name of a representative genus, with the best known ones shown in bold. Circled numbers relate to notes in the text about the informal groupings shown.

NOTES

1 **Non-vascular plants** or **bryophytes**. These plants were the first to evolve from aquatic algal ancestors and, although generally regarded as rather poorly adapted to land, mosses in particular are diverse and abundant. Bog-mosses (*Sphagnum* spp.) dominate acid peat bog vegetation and their dead remains are the main component of peat; some mosses tolerate severe cold and are dominant in polar regions and above the treeline on mountains; and the moist western parts of the British Isles probably has the richest bryophyte flora in Europe. The distinguishing features of bryophytes are summarized below:

- They have *no woody cells*, that is, cells in which the cell walls are stiffened and strengthened by deposition of the polymer **lignin**. As a result, bryophytes are all low-growing and have either a leafy shoot (mosses and some liverworts) or a flat thallus (hornworts and some liverworts), with rhizoids for attachment.

- The dominant generation, that is, the plant you see, is *the haploid gametophyte*. It produces flagellated male gametes (sperm) which swim over the moist surface and fuse with much larger female gametes (egg cells) which remain embedded in parent tissue. The diploid sporophyte develops from a zygote on the gametophyte and is visible as a stalk and spore-containing capsule (Figue 1.32).

Figure 1.32 A moss plant (*Tortula muralis*) showing the leafy shoot of the gametophyte and the stalk and spore capsule of the sporophyte generation growing from it.

2 **Vascular plants** or tracheophytes. All plants *except* bryophytes are described as vascular plants because they possess cells (forming the **vascular system**) specialized for the transport of water and dissolved materials around the plant. The leaf veins are part of this system. The water-conducting cells have tough lignified walls (see (1) above) and, together with thick-walled lignified fibre cells they perform a *support* function, allowing plants to reach a large size. In contrast to bryophytes, the *dominant generation in all modern vascular plants is the diploid sporophyte*. The haploid gametophyte is much smaller and structurally simpler; in later-evolved groups it is greatly reduced.

3 **Seedless vascular plants** are an artificial group comprising five phyla, of which the only ones you are likely to have seen are ferns and **horsetails** (Sphenophyta). The common horsetail (*Equisetum arvense*) is a weed of gardens and disturbed land. Apart from the ferns, which are relicts of a glorious past, all other phyla in this group contain relatively few modern species: the dense forests of the Carboniferous and Permian periods were dominated by tree lycopods and sphenophytes that are now a major component of coal deposits.

Members of this group release haploid spores from a variety of specialized structures (e.g. see Figure 1.33) and the spores germinate to give an independent, usually small and delicate gametophyte, where sexual reproduction occurs. Independently within lycopods and ferns, some plants have evolved **heterospory**, which means that there are two types of spores: large megaspores which develop into a female gametophyte, producing egg cells; and small microspores which develop into a male gametophyte, producing male gametes.

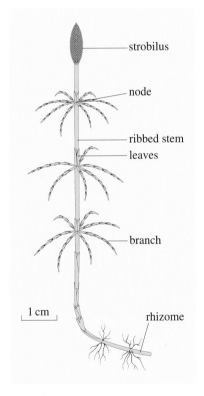

Figure 1.33 A shoot from the diploid sporophyte of a horsetail (*Equisetum sylvaticum*) with a terminal cone or strobilus in which meiosis occurs and haploid spores are produced.

4   The evolution of seeds, which are the defining characteristic of **seed plants**, is regarded as a major advance in the adaptation of plants to life on land. A **seed** is a structure borne on the diploid sporophyte and contains a diploid embryo plus stored food and protective seed coats. It functions to disperse, protect and nourish the sporophyte embryo. Independent gametophytes do not occur in seed plants and, instead, there is an extreme form of heterospory (see (3) above), with the megaspore retained and developing on the parent sporophyte within an **ovule**. The microspores are also retained and male gametophytes are dispersed from the parent sporophyte in the form of thick-walled **pollen** grains, which germinate to produce a tube through which a male gamete can reach the egg cell. A simplified version of sexual reproduction in angiosperms is shown in Figure 1.34. The end result, however, is that all requirements for a moist habitat in which sperm swim to egg cells are abolished.

5   **Gymnosperms** include four phyla of seed plants. Most are trees and they dominated vegetation in the Jurassic and early Cretaceous but are today represented by fewer than 1000 species. So this group is another with a glorious past and, like the seedless vascular plants, contributed substantially to coal deposits. **Conifers** are the best known group and are also ecologically important, dominating large areas of northern boreal forest as well as being widely planted for timber in Europe. Ovules and pollen are produced in flower-like structures (which are not true flowers) and the seeds are produced in cones. The name gymnosperm means 'naked seeds' and reflects the fact that the seeds are not surrounded by layers of sporophyte tissue as they are in angiosperms.

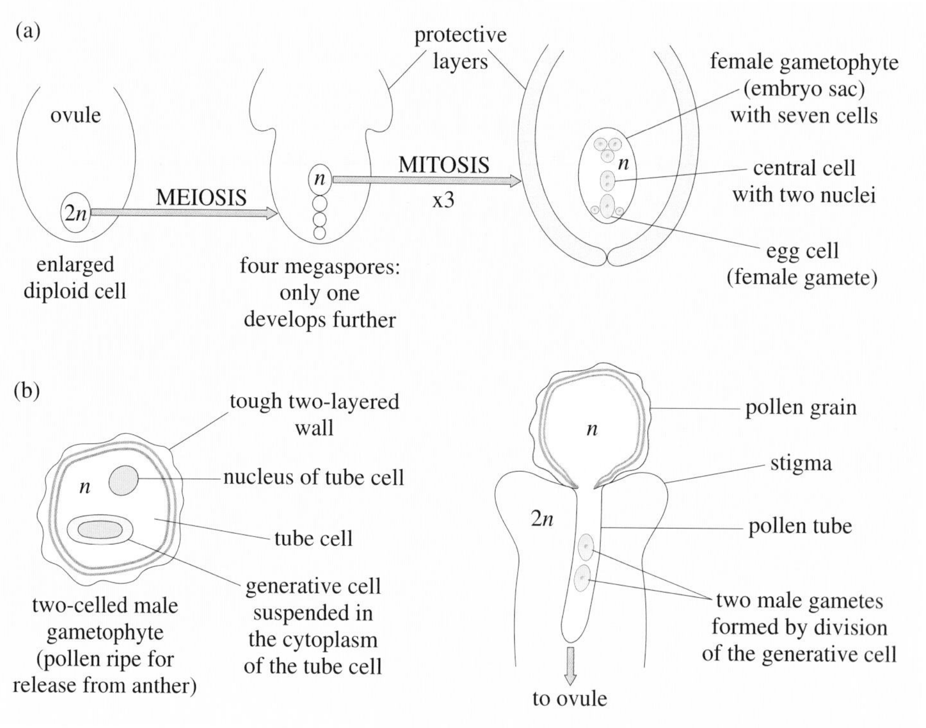

Figure 1.34 A simplified version of sexual reproduction in angiosperms. (a) Development of the female gametophyte within an ovule on the parent sporophyte. Megaspores are formed after meiosis and one then develops into a female gametophyte which contains a female gamete (egg cell). (b) Germination of a pollen grain (a two-celled male gametophyte) to produce a pollen tube which grows down to the ovule; two male gametes move down the pollen tube and one fuses with the egg cell to produce a zygote.

6 **Flowering plants** or **angiosperms** are the crowning glory of the plant kingdom and largely displaced gymnosperms during the Cretaceous period. They are more diverse in terms of species, structure and ecology than any other plant group and central to their success was the evolution of the following characteristics:

• structures (**flowers**) that facilitate sexual reproduction and allow animals, particularly insects, to transport pollen between flowers;

• very well protected and nourished seeds that are surrounded by maternal tissues which form a **fruit**. Seeds are usually dispersed within a fruit and animals may be involved in dispersal;

• a wide array of chemical compounds known as *secondary products*, which include alkaloids such as nicotine. Other plant phyla make secondary products but they are less diverse than in angiosperms. The main function of these chemicals appears to be deterrence of animal grazers which, in turn, have evolved mechanisms for detoxifying or tolerating the deterrents.

All three of these characteristics have involved **coevolution** between animals and plants, that is, a process in which two species exert selective forces on each other so that both undergo evolutionary change. You should therefore be able to appreciate that much of the diversity seen in angiosperms, and especially the variety and beauty of flowers, have their origins in animal-plant coevolution.

It is worth describing briefly here the main groups into which angiosperms are classified. Until the early 1990s, there were just two groups, ranked either as classes or sub-phyla: the Monocotyledones, informally termed **monocots**, which includes the grass, lily and orchid families; and the Dicotyledones, informally termed **dicots**, which includes the buttercup, daisy and cabbage families. The names derive from the number of *cotyledons* or seed leaves, which are often food storage structures within seeds: monocots have one cotyledon and dicots have two. New comparative and molecular evidence, however, has shown that some plants previously classed as dicots belong to neither group but are ancestral to both. These ancient plants include magnolia trees and the whole group, comprising about 3% of the total angiosperm species, is commonly referred to as **magnoliids**. The residual dicots have been renamed the Eudicotyledones or **eudicots** (*eu* being Greek for 'well').

With the help of the above notes, Figure 1.31 and the *GLO* CD-ROM, you should be able to become reasonably familiar with the plant kingdom and know how to find information about it.

1.5.3 THE KINGDOM FUNGI

Fungi are probably less familiar to you than plants, so first make a list of all the organisms that you would describe as fungi.

Cultivated mushrooms are an obvious start and there are also many 'wild fungi', including brackets on trees and a great variety of 'toadstools'. In addition, you might have thought of the microscopic and, often, disease- or decay-causing fungi such as mildews, rusts and moulds and the yeasts that are used in making wine and beer. The aim here is to provide only a brief outline defining what fungi are and do, so that you can make comparisons with other kingdoms. To this end, Table 1.1 provides an opportunity to list the key characteristics of each eukaryotic kingdom. Plant characteristics are already listed and you should try to fill in the rest of the table as you read on. A completed table is provided on p. 54.

THE NATURE OF FUNGI

Like plants, fungi have diversified mainly on land and they occur in soil and in or on the tissues of other organisms (living or dead) virtually everywhere. The fact that you rarely *see* fungi except as fuzzy patches of mould or the occasional toadstool reflects the nature of the fungal 'body' and their mode of life. The majority of fungi consist of microscopic filaments or **hyphae** (singular, **hypha**) which grow at their tips and branch repeatedly (Figure 1.35). Hyphae have rigid cell walls in which the main structural component is **chitin**, a polysaccharide which is also found in the outer skeleton of insects. The mass of hyphae is called a **mycelium** (plural, **mycelia**).

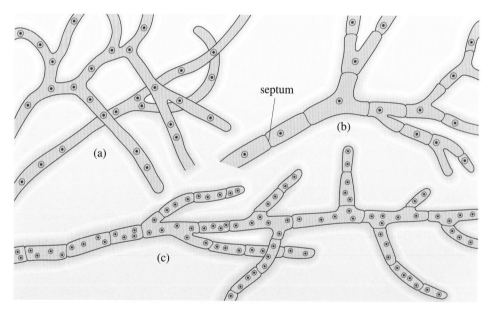

Figure 1.35 Types of fungal hyphae: (a) non-septate (coenocytic); (b) septate with one nucleus per compartment; (c) septate with many nuclei per compartment.

○ From Figure 1.35, should fungi be described as unicellular or multicellular?

● Neither term provides a precise description of the situation in fungi but multicellular is closer to reality and is how fungi are usually described.

Figure 1.35 shows that hyphae may have partitions or *septa* (singular, *septum*) which divide up hyphae into cell-like compartments. However the 'cells' may have one or several nuclei and the septa may be perforated, which allows nuclei and cytoplasm to move along hyphae. In the extreme case (Figure 1.35a) there are no septa at all and this state is described as **coenocytic** (from the Greek words for 'shared' and 'vessel'). Some fungi spend part of their life cycle as a unicellular or

Table 1.1   The key characteristics of the eukaryote kingdoms.

	Characteristic	Plants	Fungi	Animals	Protoctists
1	Unicellular (U) or multicellular (M)	M			
2	Has a rigid cell wall	yes (cellulose)			
3	Dominant or feeding stage of life cycle: haploid (H) diploid (D)	D (except bryophytes)			
4	Mode of nutrition: autotrophic (A) heterotrophic (H)	A (except parasites)			
5	Type of heterotrophic feeding: absorption (Abs) engulfs/takes in particles (Par)				
6	Main habitats: aquatic freshwater (AF) aquatic marine (AM) terrestrial above ground (TA) terrestrial below ground (TB)	TA (a few AF and AM)			
7	Forms an embryo	yes			

yeast form (Figure 1.36) and the best known yeast, *Saccharomyces cerevisiae*, which is used in baking, wine and beer making and as a laboratory organism (see Chapter 3), only rarely becomes hyphal (it does so under conditions of extreme starvation).

The hyphal branches of a fungal mycelium have an enormous surface area and here lies the clue to the fungal way of life. Fungi are *heterotrophic absorbers*. Because of their rigid walls, they cannot engulf particles and instead, as hyphae spread in or over a substratum, enzymes are secreted that break down organic molecules releasing soluble products which can be absorbed to provide nourishment. The significance of fungal activity in breaking down dead organic matter cannot be overstated because it is central to the process of *decomposition*, whereby mineral nutrients are cycled within ecosystems. Many fungi also live in partnership with plants or algae, obtaining energy (as organic molecules) from the autotroph and usually supplying inorganic nutrients such as phosphate ions in return. This **symbiotic** mode of life (**symbiosis** means 'living together') is very ancient: some early fossil plants from the Devonian, over 400 Ma ago, have been found with fossilized fungal partners and it has been suggested that fungal symbionts played a major role in the invasion of land by plants — perhaps another example of coevolution.

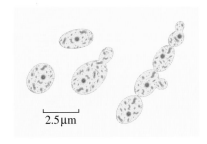

2.5 µm

Figure 1.36 The structure of yeast, *Saccharomyces cerevisiae*.

Whatever their mode of life, however, the basic mycelial structure of fungi remains much the same. So although, like bacteria, fungi show great metabolic diversity in the substrates they use, the structural diversity of the feeding stage is limited. Where fungi do show morphological diversity is in the structures that produce and disperse **spores**, which are agents of reproduction (both sexual and asexual) and dispersal. Figure 1.37 shows some examples of spore-producing systems in fungi and you can see more on the *GLO* CD-ROM. Notice that large, visible fungal structures such as mushrooms are aggregations of hyphae where haploid spores are produced following nuclear fusion and meiosis as part of sexual reproduction.

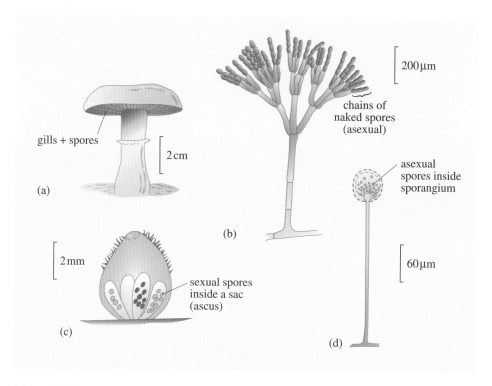

Figure 1.37 Examples of spore-producing structures in fungi. (a) A mushroom, *Agaricus* sp., a basidiomycete; sexual spores are produced on the gills. (b) An ascomycete mould, *Penicillium* sp., with asexual spores. (c) An ascomycete fungus *Podospora*, with sexual spores produced inside a sac from which they are ejected. (d) A zygomycete bread mould, *Mucor* sp., with asexual spores produced within a sporangium at the tip of a vertical hypha.

○ Are such mushroom spores equivalent to the spores produced in plants?

● Yes, in that both are produced following meiosis.

The asexual spores shown in Figure 1.37 are produced by mitosis and are also haploid because, unlike the majority of plants and animals, *most fungi spend most of their life cycle as haploids*.

By now you should be able to fill in most of the fungi column in Table 1.1 and produce your own definition of what a fungus is. What we consider to be the defining features of fungi are listed below:

- They are eukaryotic, multicellular or coenocytic heterotrophs that diversified mainly on land.
- Their structure is usually filamentous with hyphae having rigid, chitinous walls.
- Feeding is by absorption.
- Reproduction and dispersal are by means of spores, which are usually non-motile, and most of the life cycle is haploid.

ORIGINS AND CLASSIFICATION OF FUNGI

There are very few fossil remains of fungi so their origins and relationship to other kingdoms are still uncertain. A best guess estimate is that fungi evolved about 500 Ma ago. Molecular sequence studies in the 1990s indicated that the closest relatives of fungi are animals and that both kingdoms may have evolved from similar flagellated protoctists (see Figure 1.25). An earlier and still widely held view is that fungi are plant-like, possibly descendants of red algae, and we still find fungi discussed in botanical textbooks. In addition, a number of groups that are now known to be protoctists were classified as fungi and are still studied by mycologists.

○ Recall or find out from Figure 1.25 and the *GLO* CD-ROM which protoctist phyla were once regarded as fungi.

● The cellular slime moulds in phylum 3 and non-cellular slime moulds (phylum 5, Myxomycota); also phyla 17, 19 and 20. Phylum 19 contains the water moulds or oomycetes (Oomycota) which, in outward appearance and mode of nutrition, are indistinguishable from fungi. Their similarity, however, is another example of convergent evolution: the two groups are not closely related.

Fungi are now classified into four phyla (Figure 1.38) although there is disagreement about inclusion of the chytrids (pronounced ki'trids), the Chytridiomycota, which are sometimes regarded as protoctists. Chytrids certainly appear to have evolved earlier than the other fungal lineages and are the only group in which flagellated spores and gametes are formed. The life cycle and mode of sexual reproduction are the main characters used to classify fungi and it is the *lack* of sexual stages that has resulted in some 17 000 species of fungi being grouped in taxonomic limbo — the unattached branch on the right in Figure 1.38. Most of these so called **anamorphic** fungi are thought to be ascomycetes. A few of the fungal types and structures in different phyla can be seen from the common names in Figure 1.38 and illustrations in Figure 1.37 and others can be seen on the *GLO* CD-ROM.

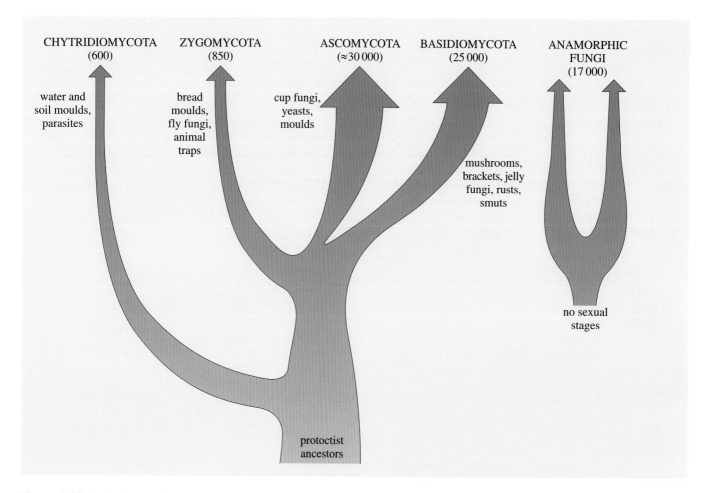

CHYTRIDIOMYCOTA
(600)

water and
soil moulds,
parasites

ZYGOMYCOTA
(850)

bread
moulds,
fly fungi,
animal
traps

ASCOMYCOTA
(≈30 000)

cup fungi,
yeasts,
moulds

BASIDIOMYCOTA
(25 000)

mushrooms,
brackets, jelly
fungi, rusts,
smuts

ANAMORPHIC
FUNGI
(17 000)

no sexual
stages

protoctist
ancestors

Figure 1.38 A phylogeny of the kingdom Fungi. Names of phyla are shown in capital letters with the estimated numbers of species in each given below.

Overall, the Fungi have fewer phyla than any other eukaryote kingdom and in this sense are the least diverse. They seem to have exploited the absorptive mode of life on land to the full and to have been living in much the same way throughout their known evolutionary history. Thus fossil remains of the three major phyla (zygomycetes, ascomycetes and basidiomycetes) occur in rocks aged between 380 and 438 Ma old and no new phlya have appeared since this period. The contrast with plants (Figure 1.31), in which many new phyla evolved between 400 and 150 Ma ago, is striking. The contrast with animals, which are considered next, is even more striking.

1.5.4 ANIMALS, THE KINGDOM ANIMALIA

The animal kingdom is the oldest, most diverse (in terms of numbers of phyla) and most numerous (in terms of numbers of species) of the three multicellular eukaryotic kingdoms. If you look ahead to Figure 1.42 you can see that Animalia contains more phyla than the plant and fungal kingdoms put together, and if you think about the range of animal forms — earthworms, insects, starfish, snails and birds, to name just a few — then it becomes clear that animals have evolved far more ways of constructing a body. Morphological diversity is much greater in animals. The origins and nature of this diversity are considered briefly here, but first, some general definitions of animals are needed.

WHAT IS AN ANIMAL?

From general knowledge and earlier studies you can probably fill in several of the rows for animals in Table 1.1. Do this now and then complete (or change) your answer as you read on. Animals, which are also known as **Metazoa**, meaning 'after or later animals', are defined by the following criteria:

- They are multicellular eukaryotes whose cells *lack* a rigid wall and they may attain a high degree of specialization with elaborate systems of communication between tissues (rows 1 and 2).

- They are mostly *diploid* organisms (although there are exceptions: some animals, including certain lizards and worker honey bees, are haploid) with no alternation of generations (row 3).

- They are all *heterotrophs* and usually feed by taking in *particulate food*, which is digested within a gut. Of great value in obtaining food is the power of *movement*, which is well developed in animals. There are many exceptions, however: in some phyla the gut has been secondarily lost, for example, internal parasites such as tapeworms do not usually digest food but absorb predigested material through the body wall; some animals form symbiotic associations with autotrophs and receive nourishment in the form of soluble molecules from their partner. Sponges (phylum Porifera) never evolved a gut (rows 4 and 5).

- They are more widely distributed than any other eukaryotic kingdom and occur in all the habitats listed in Table 1.1. Some animals, notably the insects, and terrestrial vertebrates, have diversified in a spectacular way on land but *animals evolved in, and the majority of their phyla are still confined to, the sea*. There is a marked contrast here with plants and fungi, which diversified almost entirely on land (row 6).

- They also commonly show sexual reproduction and, during embryo development from a fertilized egg, form a *blastula*, a hollow ball of cells (Figure 1.39 and row 7).

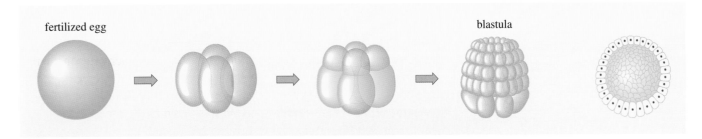

Figure 1.39 A generalized pattern of early animal development from fertilized egg to blastula. The figure at far right is a section through a blastula.

ORIGINS AND DIVERSITY OF ANIMALS

To put into perspective the greater age of the animal kingdom (compared with plants and fungi) and also the considerable controversy that still rages about precisely *when* animals originated and diversified, look at Figure 1.40.

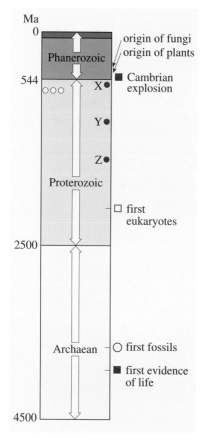

Figure 1.40 A timescale of Earth's history showing some significant events in biological evolution. The Cambrian 'explosion' is a period of rapid animal diversification (see text); X, Y and Z represent dates suggested for the first major divergence of animal phyla; and the yellow dots show the age of fossil animal embryos discovered in 1998.

Fossil evidence shows that the main types of animal phyla (and many other types that became extinct) had evolved by or during the period of rapid diversification known as the Cambrian 'explosion', 540–525 Ma ago, and all were marine. Points X, Y and Z are alternative suggested dates for the first major branch point in animal evolution, corresponding to the point labelled (B) in Figure 1.42 when bilaterally symmetrical animals (the Bilateria) began to diversify. Dates X (565 Ma) and Y (670 Ma) are based on fossil evidence, and Z (1200 Ma) on molecular evidence, all published in the period 1996–1998. Some of the beautifully preserved fossil embryos discovered in China in 1998 (yellow dots on Figure 1.40) are shown in Figure 1.41.

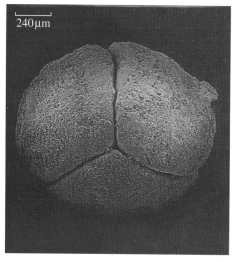

Figure 1.41 Fossil animal embryos from deposits in southern China: (a) four-cell stage; (b) later stage in blastula development.

○ These embryos are generally accepted to be of bilaterian animals. If true, which of the dates X, Y and Z is *least* likely to be correct?

● X, because the embryos were fossilized *before* this date.

The discrepancy between dates Y and Z is still enormous (about 540 Ma) and there is still no consensus about which (if either) is correct. So all we can say is that animals probably originated at some time *before* the branch point of 670 Ma ago; a date in the range 900 to 1200 Ma ago is suggested in Figure 1.42, labelled (A), which is over 400 Ma before plants or fungi originated.

Now look more carefully at Figure 1.42 on page 50, which is a simplified version of one of several possible schemes for classifying animal phyla into large groups, omitting all names of phyla except those commonly mentioned. You are not expected to memorize this scheme but may find it useful when animal types are mentioned and when you use the *GLO* CD-ROM. Figure 1.42 shows clearly what was meant when we described animals as having a high diversity of phyla!

Notice in Figure 1.42 that three branches emerge at an early point on the family tree, including the relatively familiar **sponges** (Porifera) and the corals and jellyfish (**Cnidaria**), whose bodies are radially symmetrical. Cells of most sponges bear a remarkable resemblance to a group of protoctists known as the choanoflagellates (pronounced koa′noflagellates) (Figure 1.43) and sponges are thought to have evolved from this group. Still unresolved, however, is the protoctist ancestry of other animals. Animals might be monophyletic but it is also possible that other choanoflagellates or even completely different protoctist flagellates gave rise to most of the animal lineages.

There are several mutually incompatible schemes for arranging the animal phyla into higher categories, based upon early embryonic development, mode of growth, feeding structures, and other characters. Figure 1.42 shows one such scheme, but this grouping is likely to change in the future. From the numbers of species shown for each phylum or class in Figure 1.42 you can see that insects are, by a very large margin, the most species-diverse of all animal groups.

The phylum Chordata includes the most familiar of all animals, the **vertebrates** (subphylum Vertebrata). Most vertebrate species are fish, but the rest comprise all those groups — amphibians, reptiles, birds and mammals — which successfully colonized *land*. Relatively few other animal phyla have achieved this feat, particularly the ability to live above ground in air. Flatworms, annelids and nematodes are all abundant in moist, protected habitats, such as the soil or bodies of other organisms, but only insects, spiders, a few crustaceans (e.g. woodlice) and one group of molluscs (the gastropods, e.g. slugs and snails) are abundant in habitats above ground. The common tendency to refer to animals as vertebrates, 'with backbones', or **invertebrates,** 'without backbones', as though they were the two major groupings of animals of equal weight is misleading, although still a useful and widely used distinction that reflects important physiological and morphological contrasts between them.

○ From Figure 1.42, why are vertebrates and invertebrates not equivalent terms?

● Because vertebrates are only one subphylum (although sometimes classified as a phylum) whereas all other phyla and the great majority of species are invertebrates.

The classification of animals into so many different phyla reflects the fact that each phylum has a distinctive **body plan**, that is, a particular arrangement of tissues and organs that allows the whole animal to function effectively. A point worth making here is that a body plan imposes structural limits on a phylum. For example, the rigid outer layer (exoskeleton) and the non-circulatory respiration system, which are features of the arthropod body plan, limit overall size for terrestrial species because it becomes impossible to support and move the heavy body and supply all parts with oxygen: ten metre-long ants could only exist in horror films. Plants and fungi, by contrast, are more flexible and have relatively few constraints on size. Fungi have nothing equivalent to a body plan and most plants have one major 'body' plan where size is constrained only by the amount and distribution of woody supporting tissues.

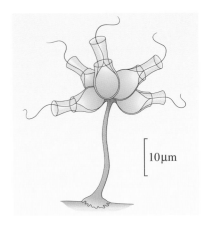

10 μm

Figure 1.43 A colony of choanoflagellates, protoctists which are thought to be ancestral to sponges and possibly to other animals.

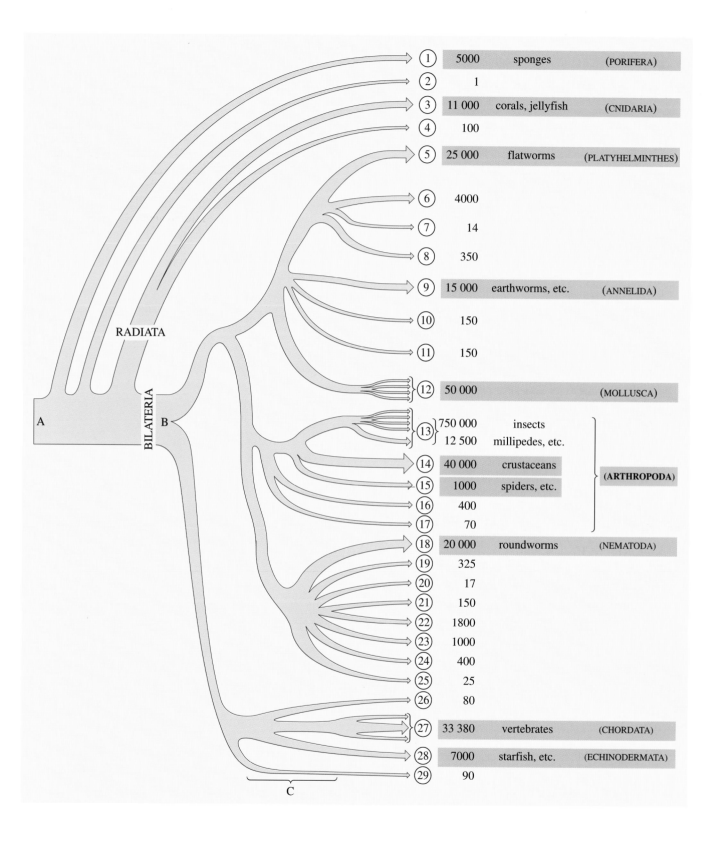

1   PORIFERA

2   PLACOZOA

3   CNIDARIA

4   CTENOPHORA

5   PLATYHELMINTHES

6   BRYOZOA

7   PHORONIDA

8   BRACHIOPODA

9   ANNELIDA

10 POGONOPHORA

11 ENTOPROCTA

12 MOLLUSCA

13 MANDIBULATA

14 CRUSTACEA

15 CHELICERATA   arthropods can be treated as a superphylum or classified as one phylum, ARTHROPODA

16 TARDIGRADA

17 ONYCHOPHERA

18 NEMATODA

19 NEMATOMORPHA

20 PRIAPULIDA

21 KINORHYNCHA

22 ROTIFERA

23 ACANTHOCEPHALA

24 GASTROTRICHIA

25 LORICIFERA

26 HEMICHORDATA

27 CHORDATA

28 ECHINODERMATA

29 CHAETOGNATHA

Figure 1.42 A phylogeny of the kingdom Animalia. Names of phyla are in capital letters, some classes or common names are given in lower case type. The numbers in circles indicate phyla (a full list of phylum names is given on this page) with the number of species in each given alongside. The horizontal axis represents time but is not drawn to scale and letters refer to approximate dates for: (A) the origin of animals, 900–1200 Ma ago; (B) diversification of Bilateria, 670 Ma ago; (C) the Cambrian 'explosion' of phyla, 525–540 Ma ago.

The body plans of all existing animal phyla evolved before or during the Cambrian and, in contrast to plants, no new phyla are known to have evolved since that period. The processes and selective forces that led to the origins of so many animal phyla and then to phenomenal diversification within certain phyla (notably the arthropods) are questions that cannot be addressed here. In the next chapter, we explore functional diversity within the protoctists, a kingdom in which all modes of life occur — autotrophic (plant-like), fungus-like and animal-like — so that you can learn about some real examples of diversification.

If you have not already done so, you should now complete Table 1.1, a completed version of which is given as Table 1.2 on p. 54.

SUMMARY OF SECTION 1.5

1   There are four eukaryotic kingdoms. Protoctista are the most ancient kingdom (that is, first to evolve) and include all the unicellular eukaryotes and any multicellular descendants which are neither plants, animals nor fungi. They show enormous diversity of structure and mode of life and are often classified into several kingdoms. The majority possess flagella or cilia at some stage of their life cycle.

2   Protoctist lineages that evolved before the endosymbiotic acquisition of mitochondria are called the Archezoa. All are confined to habitats where there is little or no oxygen and they include the gut parasite *Giardia lamblia*.

3   Protoctists that acquired chloroplasts by endosymbiosis are called algae. Two phyla acquired chloroplasts from a cyanobacterium (primary endosymbiosis) and other phyla acquired chloroplasts later from algal (eukaryotic) endosymbionts (secondary endosymbiosis).

4   Plants (kingdom Plantae) are multicellular, eukaryotic photosynthesizers adapted primarily to life on land. They usually have sexual reproduction, develop from a diploid embryo and show an alternation of multicellular haploid and diploid generations (gametophyte and sporophyte, respectively). Mature plants are non-motile and have cells with rigid walls strengthened by cellulose.

5   Plants evolved from green algae and, except in some bryophytes, have an upright leafy shoot (the photosynthetic part) and non-green underground parts for anchorage and absorption (roots, rhizoids or modified shoots). Plant diversification and classification relate primarily to reproductive structures, life cycles and support or transport tissues.

6   Twelve plant phyla are recognized here. The oldest (i.e. first to evolve) are the non-vascular plants or bryophytes, whose three phyla have no woody or vascular conducting tissues and in which the haploid gametophyte is the dominant generation. The remaining nine phyla (vascular plants or tracheophytes) develop woody, including vascular, tissues, and are able to attain much larger sizes. The sporophyte generation is dominant and the gametophyte shows a progressive reduction from the earliest to the most recently evolved and diverse tracheophytes, the flowering plants.

7   The fungi are eukaryotic, multicellular or coenocytic heterotrophs which feed by absorption and, apart from yeasts, have a filamentous, hyphal construction. Hyphae have rigid walls strengthened by chitin, and reproduction involves spores as dispersal agents. For most of their life cycle, fungi are haploid and, like plants, they diversified mainly on land.

8   Fungi probably evolved from flagellated protoctist ancestors and are classified, mainly on the basis of their life cycle and reproductive structures, into four phyla. The earliest to evolve (chytrids) produce flagellated spores but all other fungi lack flagella.

9   Animals are multicellular, eukaryotic heterotrophs that feed mainly by consuming particulate organic matter. Their cells lack a rigid wall and may become highly specialized. Most animals are diploid and have sexual reproduction with embryo development into a blastula. Diversification has occurred mainly in the sea.

10 Animals probably originated 900–1200 Ma ago. They are classified on the basis of the arrangement of body tissues and organs, with each of the 35 (or so) phyla having a distinctive body plan which was established before or during the Cambrian.

11 The earliest animals include sponges and the radially symmetrical Cnidaria (corals and jellyfish). Other animals are bilaterally symmetrical (the Bilateria), the majority of species occurring in the arthropod phylum, mainly in the class Insecta.

REFERENCES

Shimamura, M., Yasue, H., Ohshima, K., Abe, H., Kata, H., Kishiro, T., Goto, M., Munechika, I. and Okada, N. (1997) Molecular evidence from retroposons that whales form a clade within even-toed ungulates, *Nature*, **388**, pp. 666–670.

Wilson, E. O. (1997) Introduction. In M. L. Reaka-Kudla, D. E. Wilson and E. O. Wilson (eds), *Biodiversity II: understanding and protecting our biological resources*, Joseph Henry Press, Washington, D.C.

FURTHER READING

Barnes, R. S. K. (ed.) (1998) *The Diversity of Living Organisms*, Blackwell Science, London. [A textbook giving a comprehensive description of taxonomic diversity.]

Brusca, R. C. and Brusca, G. J. (1990) *Invertebrates*, Sinauer Associates Inc., Sunderland, Massachusetts. [A textbook which includes heterotrophic protoctists but which uses a different taxonomy from that used here.]

Margulis, L. and Schwarz, K. V. (1998) (3rd edn), *Five Kingdoms: an illustrated guide to the phyla of life on Earth*, W. H. Freeman & Company, New York. [Gives a comprehensive description of phyla in all domains.]

Raven, P. H., Evert, R. F. and Eichhorn, S. E. (1999) (6th edn) *Biology of Plants*, W. H. Freeman & Company, New York. [A well illustrated and very readable textbook that describes not only the main types of plants but also fungi and algae.]

Table 1.2 Characteristics of the eukaryotic kingdoms.

	Characteristic	Plants	Fungi	Animals	Protoctists
1	Unicellular (U) or multicellular (M)	M	M (coenocytic) U (yeasts)	M	U Some M
2	Has a rigid cell wall	yes (cellulose)	yes (chitin)	no	yes (most algae) no (the rest)
3	Dominant or feeding stage of life cycle: haploid (H) diploid (D)	D (except bryophytes)	H	D	H or D
4	Mode of nutrition: autotrophic (A) heterotrophic (H)	A (except parasites)	H	H	A or H
5	Type of heterotrophic feeding: absorption (Abs) engulfs/takes in particles (Par)		Abs	Par (a few Abs)	Abs and Par
6	Main habitats: aquatic freshwater aquatic marine (AM) terrestrial above ground (TA) terrestrial below ground (TB)	**TA** (a few AF (AF) and AM)	TA, **TB** (chytrids AF and a few AM)	**AM**, TA, TB, AF	AM, AF, TB (rarely TA)
7	Forms an embryo	yes	no	yes (blastula)	no

DIVERSITY IN PROTOCTISTS

2.1 INTRODUCTION: INNOVATION AND OPPORTUNITY

In Chapter 1 we considered the origins of domains and kingdoms and looked briefly at diversification within kingdoms. This chapter focuses on diversity in one kingdom, the Protoctista, which diversified mainly over the period from 2000 to 500 Ma ago, and gave rise to the other three eukaryotic kingdoms. The range of life-styles in protoctists encompasses those found in these other kingdoms — plant-like autotrophs and animal- and fungus-like heterotrophs — so the protoctists provide a good case study that lays the foundation for later studies. They are also an abundant and important component of the modern biota, especially in the soil and the oceans: microscopic algae, for example, are the main primary producers in oceans and are believed to exert a significant effect on the Earth's climate.

The nature of protoctist diversity is explored in Sections 2.2–2.6 but we need to think first about *context*. What were the earliest protoctists like and what sorts of prokaryotes were also present (the biological starting point)? What was the environment like and how did it change over the period of diversification? If this background can be filled in, it becomes possible to think about a more interesting question, which is *why* protoctist diversification occurred. Two major influences must have been involved:

- *biological*, with innovations such as the evolution of flagella and the acquisition of chloroplasts allowing organisms to adopt new life-styles and exploit new environments, and

- *environmental*, with changes such as massive geological disturbances or chemical changes in the atmosphere acting to select new types of organisms, and the evolution of new types of organisms influencing the survival and evolution of other types.

Biological innovations and environmental change would have acted together to promote diversification, although their relative importance is difficult to assess. In the rest of this section we give an overview of current ideas about the organisms and environment on the early Earth which provided the context for protoctist evolution.

2.1.1 CHANGING ENVIRONMENTS: PHOTOSYNTHESIS AND OXYGEN

Figure 2.1 (overleaf) shows a best-estimate of links between episodes of biological innovation, diversification and environmental change, with approximate dates, up to the Cambrian period. Much of the information in this section is summarized in Figure 2.1, so look at it briefly now and study it more carefully after reading the section.

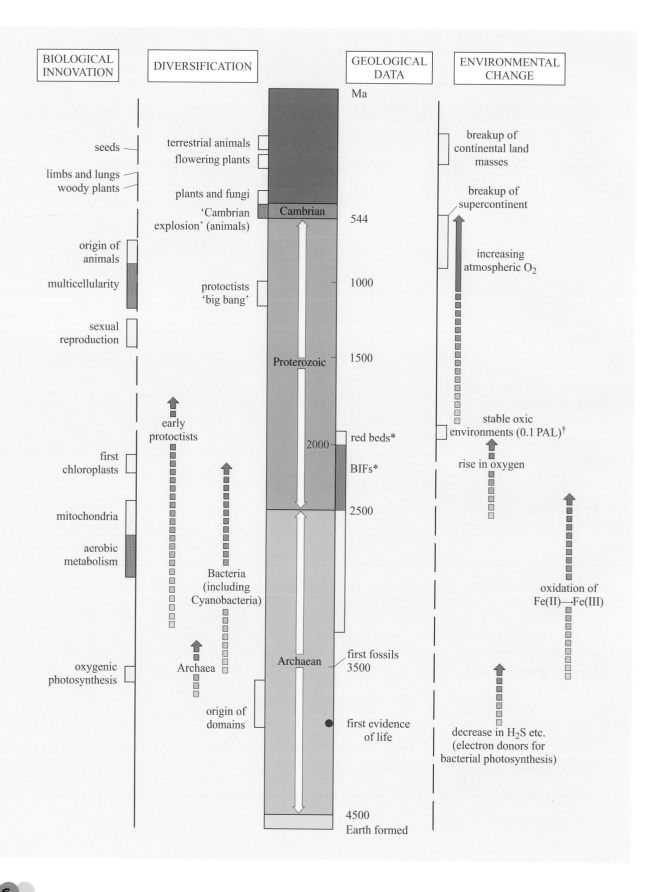

| BIOLOGICAL INNOVATION | DIVERSIFICATION | GEOLOGICAL DATA | ENVIRONMENTAL CHANGE |

Ma

seeds

terrestrial animals
flowering plants

breakup of continental land masses

limbs and lungs
woody plants

plants and fungi

breakup of supercontinent

'Cambrian explosion' (animals)

Cambrian

544

origin of animals

increasing atmospheric O_2

multicellularity

protoctists 'big bang'

1000

sexual reproduction

Proterozoic

1500

early protoctists

first chloroplasts

red beds*

2000

stable oxic environments (0.1 PAL)†

rise in oxygen

BIFs*

mitochondria

2500

aerobic metabolism

Bacteria (including Cyanobacteria)

oxidation of Fe(II)→Fe(III)

oxygenic photosynthesis

Archaea

Archaean

first fossils
3500

origin of domains

first evidence of life

decrease in H_2S etc. (electron donors for bacterial photosynthesis)

4500
Earth formed

Three general points emerge from Figure 2.1 which put the eukaryote kingdoms in their proper perspective and emphasize the importance of protoctists.

1   From the time when life first evolved on Earth (about 4000 Ma ago) to the present, prokaryotes were the dominant organisms for at least the first 2000 Ma — half the time available for biological evolution.

2   For nearly 2000 Ma (from 2700 to 900 Ma ago), protoctists were the only eukaryotes present, so they have been around for three to five times longer than any other eukaryote kingdom.

3   Animals, plants and fungi are relative newcomers which originated and diversified in the last 500 to 900 Ma — one-eighth to one-quarter of the time available for evolution.

To set the scene for protoctist evolution you need to look at the lower half of Figure 2.1, beginning on the left-hand side. The first biological innovation listed here is *oxygenic photosynthesis*, the kind of photosynthesis that evolved in cyanobacteria (Figure 1.19) and involves the release of oxygen from water (Section 1.3). There was no free oxygen on the early Earth. In oxygenic photosynthesis water acts as a source of electrons for the light reactions and a wonderfully convenient and abundant source it is. However, it is chemically very difficult to remove electrons from water and other photosynthetic bacteria (shown in Figure 1.19) use other sources of electrons, such as hydrogen sulphide or sulphur. It is easier to remove electrons from (i.e. oxidize) these compounds, which were relatively abundant on the early Earth, although not nearly so widespread and abundant as water. So the best scientific guess is that *non-oxygenic photosynthesizers*, similar to the present-day purple bacteria and green sulphur bacteria (which do *not* release oxygen), were dominant until about 3500 Ma ago. The selective pressure that led to the evolution of oxygenic photosynthesis in cyanobacteria was, we believe, the decreasing availability of suitable electron donors, which is listed as the first environmental change on the right side of Figure 2.1.

○   From Figure 2.1, did the Earth's atmosphere change from being anoxic (without oxygen) to oxic (with oxygen) immediately following the evolution of oxygenic photosynthesis?

●   No: atmospheric O_2 did not begin to rise until about 2500 Ma ago (1000 Ma later) and not until 2000 Ma ago were stable oxic environments available, but with only about one-tenth the present levels of O_2.

Fossil evidence shows that cyanobacteria increased, diversified and came to dominate the oceans during the Archaean period, so what became of all the oxygen that they released?

○   What answer is suggested in Figure 2.1?

●   The oxygen was 'mopped up' by the oxidation of soluble inorganic ions such as iron (II) (ferrous, Fe^{2+}), which was abundant in the early oceans: the iron (II) would be converted into iron (III) (ferric, Fe^{3+}) oxides or hydroxides, which are relatively insoluble, rust-coloured materials.

Figure 2.1   Estimated times up to the end of the Cambrian period of episodes of significant biological innovation, diversification and environmental change. *These terms are defined in the text. †PAL = present atmospheric level.

This **'iron sink' hypothesis** is supported by geological evidence, notably the presence of extensive deposits of Fe(III)-rich material in the form of banded iron formations (BIFs) and red beds (Figure 2.1). So iron oxidation certainly contributed to the removal of oxygen but it also seems likely that bacteria evolved that were capable of *using* (and thereby removing) oxygen. *Aerobic metabolism evolved* (left side of Figure 2.1).

Early aerobic heterotrophs must have been *facultative*, i.e. they could manage without oxygen if they had to (in contrast to *obligate* aerobes, which cannot); and they must have survived with vanishingly low concentrations of free oxygen. A shorthand term for such organisms is **amphiaerobes** (amphi being Greek for 'both' or 'of both kinds'). It is thought likely that the ancestor of eukaryotic mitochondria was an amphiaerobe and Figure 2.1 lists the acquisition of mitochondria (by endosymbiosis, Chapter 1) as the third major biological innovation.

You now have some idea of what conditions on Earth were like and which organisms were present when protoctists first appeared in the oceans and started to diversify: the environment was still anoxic and cyanobacteria were dominant, although many heterotrophic Bacteria (including amphiaerobes) and Archaea were present. Ideas about the origin and nature of early protoctists were discussed in Chapter 1 (Section 1.5) but the only real clues come from studying the Archezoa, the most ancient protoctist lineages that have no mitochondria.

ARCHEZOANS AS A MODEL FOR EARLY PROTOCTISTS

The defining characteristics of archezoans can be listed as:

- anaerobic metabolism and an absence of mitochondria (hence an alternative name for the group is the amitochondriates);
- a flexible outer surface for all or most of their life cycle and a very simple system of internal membranes;
- possession of a nucleus;
- possession of flagella in most, but not all, species;
- distinctive molecular sequences (in the species examined) which indicate their ancient origins.

However, you can see from Figure 2.2 that beyond this basic characterization archezoans vary widely in structure. In addition, some show neither proper mitosis, meiosis nor sexual reproduction, whereas others show all three; and while some are free-living, many are highly specialized parasites that live, for example, in the guts or cells of mammals.

○ Which archezoan, mentioned in Chapter 1, is a parasite of mammalian guts ?

● *Giardia lamblia* (Section 1.5).

Only at a late stage in their evolutionary history could these parasites have evolved adaptations to this way of life, because mammals did not evolve until about 200 Ma ago. So the problem is: which features of archezoans represent the truly ancestral state and which are later-evolved adaptations? You might recall from Chapter 1 that this sort of problem is universal when trying to sort out phylogenies and the classification of higher taxa.

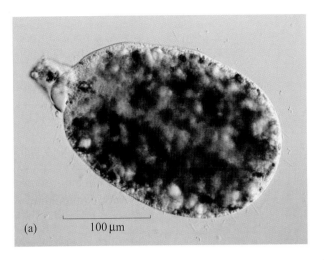

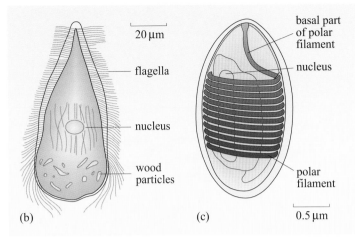

(a) 100 μm

(b) 20 μm — flagella — nucleus — wood particles

(c) basal part of polar filament — nucleus — polar filament — 0.5 μm

One example can be described to illustrate the uncertainty that exists about the nature of early archezoans, the starting point for protoctist diversification. Some archezoans in phylum 1 (Figure 1.25) contain an organelle called a **hydrogenosome**, which looks rather like a simplified form of a mitochondrion and is involved in energy metabolism and ATP synthesis but releases *hydrogen* (H_2) as a by-product (hence the name). The origin of hydrogenosomes is unknown but one view is that they are a modified form of mitochondria and may have evolved independently in other protoctists which became secondarily anaerobic. They also occur, for example, in anaerobic ciliates (phylum 10). So it is possible that early archezoans already contained a bacterial endosymbiont, presumably an amphiaerobe (see earlier), which evolved into a hydrogenosome in some, was lost in others (e.g. *Giardia*, Figure 1.26) and evolved into a mitochondrion in those species which gave rise to other protoctist lineages.

Figure 2.2 Diversity within the Archezoa. (a) Light micrograph of *Pelomyxa* sp., a large amoeboid species (phylum 1, see Figure 1.25), found in pond sediments. (b) *Trichonympha* sp. (phylum 1), which has many flagella and lives symbiotically in the guts of insects (cockroaches or termites) where it digests wood; (c) a microsporidian, *Glugea* sp. (phylum 2) which lives parasitically in muscles of a fish causing formation of a tumour.

○ In the few archezoans (including *Giardia*) where molecular sequence studies have been carried out, there are nuclear genes that are unmistakably of bacterial origin and, specifically, resemble mitochondrial genes. Is this information consistent with the above hypothesis?

● Yes: mitochondrial genes could have been transferred to the nucleus before the endosymbiont was lost. However, other explanations cannot be ruled out (for example, that hydrogenosomes were acquired independently and are not related to mitochondria; or that mitochondrial genes in *Giardia* were acquired by gene transfer much earlier).

In the early 2000s there is still no consensus about the nature of the earliest, archezoan-like protoctists. They may have lacked all organelles and their descendants acquired an amphiaerobe by endosymbiosis which evolved into a mitochondrion. Or they may have contained an amphiaerobe as described in the hypothesis above. Research into the molecular sequences of more archezoans and into the nature of hydrogenosomes is under way to try and resolve this problem. What is certain, however, is that diversification beyond archezoans relied heavily on the acquisition of mitochondria and, later, chloroplasts and we discuss this stage next.

SUMMARY OF SECTION 2.1

1   Biological innovations and environmental changes acted together to promote diversification in protoctists.

2   When protoctists first appeared and started to diversify, the atmosphere was still anoxic despite the innovation of oxygenic photosynthesis some 1000 Ma earlier. Cyanobacteria dominated the oceans but amphiaerobic Bacteria were probably also present.

3   The nature of early protoctists and which of their characteristics are now present in archezoans remains uncertain. They may have possessed hydrogenosomes (acquired by endosymbiosis) which later evolved into mitochondria. Or they may have contained no organelles except nuclei.

2.2   METABOLIC INNOVATION

In this and the next three sections we examine Protoctista as a case study in diversification. Depending on how they are classified, Protoctista, including Archezoa, comprise about 30 phyla and one way of surveying their diversity would be to describe each phylum individually. However, this would not only take too much time, it would also be repetitive because the *same kinds* of adaptations have evolved in different phyla. Instead we consider the *types* of innovation that have played particularly important roles in the diversification of protoctists, and lay foundations for later studies of animals, plants and fungi. Many of the protoctist phyla have difficult, unfamiliar names *which we do not expect you to remember* and these phyla will be referred to by the numbers shown in Figure 1.25. However, if you want or are asked to use the *GLO* CD-ROM to find out more about a phylum, you need to know its name and so Figure 2.3 lists the phylum names of the Protoctista.

In this section we consider two of the most significant metabolic innovations in protoctists: the acquisition of mitochondria and chloroplasts.

2.2.1   MITOCHONDRIA, OXYGEN AND AEROBIC METABOLISM

Early in protoctist evolution, mitochondria were acquired by endosymbiosis (Chapter 1). Irrespective of whether mitochondria evolved from a hydrogenosome or directly from an amphiaerobic bacterial partner (Section 2.1.1), they allowed protoctists to switch from anaerobic to aerobic respiration.

○   From earlier studies of aerobic respiration and anaerobic respiration (fermentation), what are the energetic advantages of the former?

●   Aerobic respiration releases several times more energy (ATP molecules) per molecule of substrate (e.g. glucose) metabolized compared with fermentation.

You can see from Figure 2.1 that atmospheric O_2 levels were rising during the early period of protoctist diversification, so there must have been strong selective pressures favouring organisms that could exploit aerobic habitats and improve their energy efficiency. Mitochondria are more than ATP factories, however,

Figure 2.3 A list of the phylum names of the Protoctista. You are not expected to remember these names. *These phyla are not described in the *GLO* CD-ROM.

ARCHEZOA (or amitochondriates) (subkingdom)

1. Archaeprotista
2. Microspora

EUPROTOCTISTA (subkingdom, the rest)

3. Rhizopoda (amoebas and cellular slime moulds, Acrasiomycetes)
4. Discomitochondria (euglenoids and kinetoplastids)
5. Myxomycota (non-cellular slime moulds, myxomycetes)
6. Rhodophyta (red algae)
7. Granuloreticulosa (forams, Foraminifera and Reticulomyxida)
8. Xenophyophora*

⟹ Superphylum Alveolata

9. Dinoflagellida (dinoflagellates)
10. Ciliophora (ciliates)
11. Apicomplexa

12. Chlorophyta (green algae)
13. Haplospora
14. Paramyxa
15. Haptophyta (haptophytes or haptomonads)
16. Cryptophyta (cryptophytes or cryptomonads)

⟹ Superphylum Stramenopila or Heterokontophyta

Opalinida*
Bicosoecida* } previously included in phylum 28

17. Hypochytridiomycota (hypochytrids)*
18. Labyrinthulata (slime nets, labyrinthulids)
19. Oomycota (water moulds, oomycetes)
20. Plasmodiophora (endoparasitic slime moulds)*
21. Chrysophyta (golden-brown algae)
22. Phaeophyta (brown algae)
23. Xanthophyta (yellow-green algae)
24. Bacillariophyta (diatoms)
25. Eustigmatophyta*

26. Myxospora
27. Actinopoda (actinopods, radiolarians)
28. Zoomastigota (zooflagellates)

▪ 'fungal' groups
▫ algal groups
□ animal-like heterotrophs

because the TCA (tricarboxylic acid) cycle, which is located in mitochondria, serves also as a useful source of molecules for synthetic pathways such as those which build amino acids. The point to appreciate here is that mitochondria greatly increased the metabolic versatility of protoctists.

There is also a downside to the appearance of free oxygen on Earth. Oxygen is potentially a lethal toxin because it can generate within cells unstable and highly reactive **free radicals**, which are generally atoms or molecules having an extra electron (for example, superoxide, $O_2^•$). Aerobic life became possible only with the evolution of defence systems against oxygen toxicity. These systems are never 100% effective, however, and modern aerobic organisms face continuing problems from oxidative damage.

Having converted to aerobic metabolism, many later protoctists reverted to anaerobic metabolism and some, for example those ciliates (phylum 10, Ciliophora) that inhabit the rumen of cattle, have lost mitochondria and contain hydrogenosomes instead. All of these revertants live in anaerobic habitats, many of which (as in the ciliates just mentioned) are inside the bodies of larger organisms that evolved much later than protoctists. So protoctist diversification into these sorts of habitats involved a *loss* of aerobic metabolism.

2.2.2 CHLOROPLASTS AND AUTOTROPHY

The next significant metabolic innovation after mitochondria was the acquisition of chloroplasts, also by endosymbiosis (Chapter 1). You can check from Figure 2.1 when the primary chloroplast endosymbiosis is thought to have occurred but it is not possible to know with any certainty when all the secondary endosymbioses described in Chapter 1 occurred. The result, however, was that several groups of protoctists independently acquired the capacity for autotrophic metabolism.

○ Pause and think *why* a capacity for autotrophy might have been advantageous for protoctists.

● The obvious point is that autotrophs can feed themselves provided they have access to light, carbon dioxide and simple inorganic nutrients; the need to seek out and compete for organic food disappears. Once protoctists could photosynthesize they had a plentiful energy source (light) and the potential to synthesize new and surplus carbohydrates which could be used to make complex structures such as cell walls and protective scales.

Chloroplasts also provide a built-in source of oxygen, facilitating aerobic metabolism, which may have been a significant advantage when external O_2 levels were still rather low. Other important properties that may have been conferred on the host include the ability to synthesize starch (a storage carbohydrate) and cellulose (a structural carbohydrate found in cell walls). Both starch and cellulose are synthesized by cyanobacteria but not by any eukaryotes that evolved before the origin of chloroplasts or that never acquired them. Most probably the genes required for starch and cellulose synthesis, which are found in some protoctist (and plant) nuclei, were transferred there from the endosymbiont.

Changing to autotrophy did, however, impose certain restrictions on protoctists because of the need for access to light. The open water forms mostly remained small and unicellular, relying on water turbulence and their very low rate of sinking to keep them close to the surface. Many shallow-water algae from coasts and fresh water diversified in a different direction, however, by evolving into large, multicellular types anchored to the bottom; we discuss them further in Section 2.5.2. Other autotrophs, particularly among the dinoflagellates (phylum 9, Dinoflagellida), keep their options open and if light levels are low or there is an abundance of suitable food feed heterotrophically. Such mixed feeders are called **mixotrophs**. In the next section, we consider the diverse ways in which heterotrophs acquire food.

SUMMARY OF SECTION 2.2

1   Acquisition of mitochondria allowed early protoctists to exploit the increasing number of aerobic habitats, improved energy metabolism and increased metabolic flexibility. At a later stage of evolution some protoctists recolonized certain anaerobic habitats and lost mitochondria.

2   Defence systems against oxygen toxicity via free radical formation evolved as atmospheric oxygen levels increased.

3   The acquisition of chloroplasts allowed a switch to autotrophy and access to light as an abundant energy source. It also provided oxygen for aerobic metabolism and new biosynthetic abilities (e.g. starch synthesis).

4   Because of the need to stay in the light, many open-water autotrophs remained as small unicells but some shallow-water species evolved into large, anchored multicellular types.

2.3   MOTILITY AND FEEDING

Motility and feeding in protoctists are considered together because they are often closely connected (movement is usually needed to catch prey, for example) and the same organs may be used for both. Two main *methods of feeding* can be distinguished:

1   absorption of completely soluble organic matter across the cell surface; feeding in this way is described as **osmotrophy** (from the Greek *osmos*, push, and *troph*, feeding: food molecules are pushed or drawn across the cell membrane);

2   engulfing solid particles of organic matter, living or dead, which are then digested inside food vacuoles within the protoctist cell; this method of feeding is called **phagocytosis**.

These feeding methods are by no means mutually exclusive and phagocytic feeders often supplement their diet by osmotrophy if they encounter high concentrations of soluble organic matter. We consider each method in turn.

2.3.1 OSMOTROPHY

Osmotrophic protoctists tend to be specialized either in terms of where they live or in their structure — and often in both — because in the few habitats where osmotrophy is feasible, i.e. where concentrations of dissolved organic substances are high, protoctists compete poorly with Bacteria. The main reason for this is that protoctists are usually the wrong size and shape. To support a cell by osmotrophy requires that the absorptive surface (i.e. surface area, S) is large relative to the cell volume, V, and this high $S{:}V$ ratio occurs only in very small cells — as in the majority of bacteria — or in cells that are strongly flattened or lobed. The $S{:}V$ ratio in the majority of protoctists is too low.

Two groups of protoctists have circumvented this problem. The first, *internal parasites*, colonize the body cavities or blood of larger organisms or, even better, colonize their cells (where there are no competing bacteria). These nutrient-rich habitats are highly suitable for protoctistan osmotrophs and several phyla are specialized to exploit them (discussed further in Section 2.6).

The other way in which osmotrophic protoctists live is by mimicking bacteria and fungi and combining small cells or filaments with **extracellular digestion**. This process involves secretion of enzymes which digest material outside the cells, the soluble products of digestion being then absorbed by osmotrophy. Phylum 19 (Oomycota, a stramenopile group, Figure 2.3) is a classic example and these oomycetes often look remarkably like filamentous fungi. They may live in water (the water moulds), in damp soil or as parasites in terrestrial plants: the potato blight which led to the Irish famine in the mid-19th century was caused by the oomycete *Phytophthora infestans*. The feeding stage of oomycetes always consists of thread-like hyphae (similar to the fungal hyphae shown in Figure 1.35) so that movement on or inside a food source is by hyphal growth. By contrast, in another stramenopile group, the *labyrinthulids* or *slime nets* (phylum 18), movement of individual cells to food sources takes place. The cells live in colonies encased in slime and shuttle to and fro along special slimeways (Figure 2.4), congregating and secreting digestive enzymes when the net encounters food (which may be dead organic matter or living cells). How the cells move is a mystery but it may be linked to the action of contractile proteins in the slime because cells are incapable of movement outside their slimeway.

Wholly osmotrophic protoctists, therefore, generally live on solid substrates or inside larger organisms where soluble organic molecules are either freely available or can be released by extracellular digestion. Apart from the slime nets, active movement of cells rarely occurs when feeding but may be important for dispersal and/or sexual reproduction. In the protoctists that feed by phagocytosis, however, active movement often plays a significant role in capturing food.

2.3.2 PHAGOCYTOSIS

Phagotrophs — organisms that feed by phagocytosis — engulf particles of food as illustrated in Figure 2.5, which also shows the **amoeboid movement** that may accompany such feeding. Indigestible remains left in the food vacuoles are expelled from the cell. The names given to the general processes of taking material into or releasing it from cells are **endocytosis** and **exocytosis** (from the

Greek *endo* meaning into and *exo*, out of *cyto*, cells). Neither process occurs in modern prokaryotes and the ability to engulf and digest food inside the cell represents a major advance that occurred early in eukaryote evolution. The absence of these processes in prokaryotes is mainly due to the presence of a rigid envelope surrounding cells of most species (although some, particularly among the Archaea, lack a cell wall). The same applies to plants and fungi but these organisms do use exocytosis to secrete materials into their cell walls because they have a much more complex system of internal membranes than do prokaryotes.

You can see from Figure 2.5 that amoeboid movement requires a flexible cell surface and the extension of lobes of cytoplasm (**pseudopodia** (singular pseudopodium), meaning 'false feet') into which the rest of the cell flows. How this kind of movement occurs is still a mystery but what seems to happen is that the outer and slightly stiffer layer of cytoplasm becomes locally more fluid allowing the inner, more fluid cytoplasm to flow outwards to form a pseudopodium. Fibrous contractile proteins that are elements of the cytoplasmic skeleton or **cytoskeleton** are thought to play a role in these fluidity changes and cell movements. Within phylum 1 of the Archezoa, the class Archamoeba has amoeboid movement and feeds largely by phagocytosis, living in damp soil and the muddy sediments of ponds. The archamoebas also possess small flagella which are non-motile, i.e. they are not involved in movement, but other archezoans within phylum 1 (e.g. see Figure 2.2b) have many well-developed flagella, some of which are used primarily for movement and the others as aids to feeding.

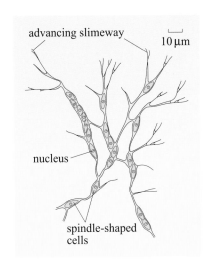

Figure 2.4 *Labyrinthula* sp. cells in slimeways.

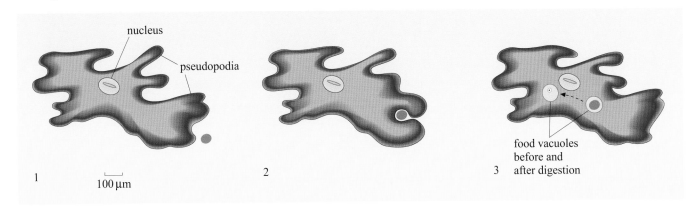

Figure 2.5 Food engulfment and amoeboid movement in *Amoeba proteus* (Rhizopoda, phylum 3).

Flagella (Chapter 1) are widespread among protoctists and there is much variation in the number per cell and the way they are held (forwards or backwards, for example) and beat to cause movement. The beating of flagella or cilia (smaller versions of flagella that occur in large numbers, Chapter 1) may propel a protoctist through water or, if the cell is anchored, cause water to flow over the cell carrying food particles towards it. Because water is a relatively viscous medium, simple to-and-fro movements of flagella do not propel small cells forwards since force generated by the back stroke is cancelled out by the forward stroke. Instead, high-speed photography has shown that flagella usually act more like outboard motors or propellers, moving with a rotary motion whilst waves of undulations pass from base to tip or tip to base (Figure 2.6a, overleaf). There are 'power' and 'recovery' strokes and flagellates 'corkscrew' through water with a helical motion. Cilia move in a cone and have a simpler motion (Figure 2.6b); the recovery stroke is weaker than the forward, power stroke so that each cilium creates a small net propulsive force and thousands of cilia beating in a concerted way can create a strong force. Ciliates (phylum 10) include the fastest movers among protoctists and because the cilia create far less disturbance in surrounding water than do larger flagella, ciliates can move smoothly through water and surprise prey: they are very efficient predators.

In all the mobile flagellates, the cell has a definite shape and a relatively rigid surface compared with amoeboid species. In the archezoans, this rigidity arose from stiffening of the cytoplasm because of cytoskeleton development and in phyla that evolved later, it also arose from the addition of extra surface structures. In all cases, the effect was to rule out amoeboid movement and phagocytosis over the cell surface as a whole. Instead these flagellates (and the ciliates) have a special area of flexible surface that is often contained within a pocket or **gullet**. Flagella or cilia specialized for feeding are positioned so that their beating produces a 'feeding current' that propels food particles into the mouth-like opening of the gullet (the **cytostome**). Phagocytosis then occurs from the gullet. There are endless variations on this basic theme, some of which are shown in Figure 2.7 where flagella and other structures whose primary function is movement and/or feeding are labelled in red. You can also see film of protoctists feeding and moving on the *GLO* CD-ROM.

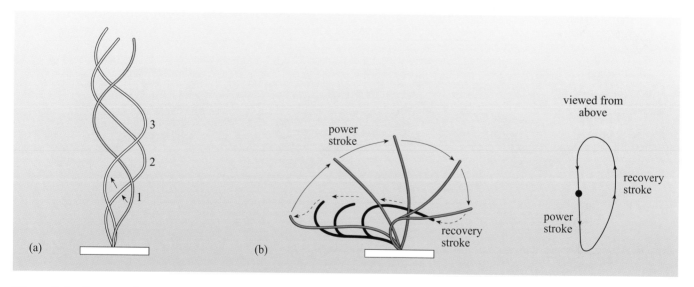

Figure 2.6 Patterns of movement in (a) an undulating flagellum showing rotary motion; (b) a cilium, showing power and recovery strokes.

○ (i) For each of (b)–(d) in Figure 2.7 identify any special features of movement/feeding structures that differ from the basic system described above; (ii) for (a)–(d) suggest how the organism feeds and the purpose of its flagella or cilia.

● (i) In both of the attached ciliates (b) and (c), cilia are grouped to form larger structures which can generate stronger currents if they beat synchronously. In (d) the two flagella are of unequal size and the larger one has hair-like outgrowths so that it appears feathery; the hairs increase the surface area of the flagellum and increase the propulsive force that it generates. (ii) (a) with its pseudopodia is clearly amoeboid, has no gullet and feeds by engulfing food anywhere on the surface; the flagellum is used for movement. (b) and (c) both have a stalk and are, therefore, anchored. Both also have a gullet and (c) has a tough outer casing so feeding must occur by wafting food towards the gullet by means of the groups of cilia. (d) has chloroplasts and is, therefore, an autotroph so the flagella must be used for movement alone.

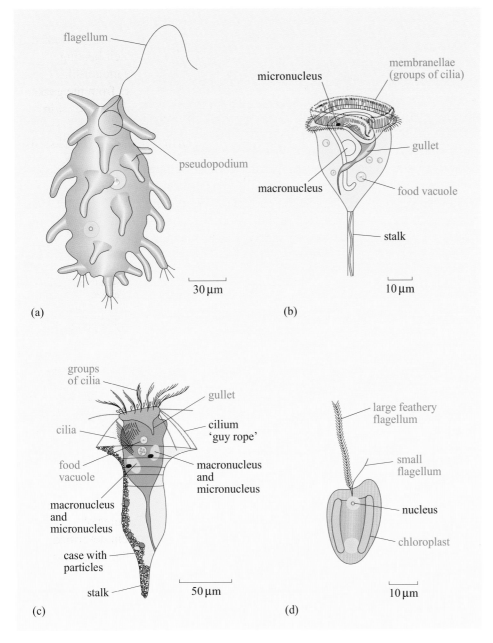

(a)

(b)

(c)

(d)

Figure 2.7 Structures involved in movement and/or feeding (red) for: (a) *Mastigamoeba* (phylum 1); (b) *Vorticella*, a ciliate (phylum 10); (c) *Tintinnopsis*, a ciliate; (d) *Ochromonas*, a chrysophyte (phylum 21).

To obtain a better understanding of how flagella and cilia work and their functions, use the search mode on *GLO* to find film of these organelles in action.

Reviewing the diversification of movement and feeding in protoctists, it seems likely that the archezoan archamoebas resemble most closely the earliest protoctists. From this type, with amoeboid movement, phagocytosis (probably with osmotrophy) and feeble flagella that acted chiefly to create feeding currents, evolved the actively swimming flagellates with stiffer outer cytoplasm and phagocytosis restricted to special feeding sites. Many specialized types of flagellates evolved from this basic flagellate lineage but, in addition, whole phyla lost flagella completely and became heterotrophic amoeboid forms (e.g. phylum 3, Rhizopoda, to which *Amoeba proteus* (Figure 2.5) belongs). Large multicellular algae retain flagella only in spores or gametes (green and brown seaweeds, phyla 12 and 22, respectively) or lack flagella completely (red algae, phylum 6).

In two other amoeboid phyla that evolved later (mainly during the Cambrian, 500–600 Ma ago) the cytoskeleton is actually developed more strongly and there are also various types of elaborate, rigid skeleton or covering. The forams (class Foraminifera within phylum 7) and the actinopods (phylum 27, Actinopoda) provide another example of convergent evolution. Both feed by means of slender pseudopodia that protrude through their rigid coverings (Figure 2.8) and are strengthened by a central rod of cytoskeletal elements. Some also use their pseudopodia for swimming or, like flexible legs for walking. We shall not describe further details of feeding in these groups but you can find out more from *GLO*. Both of these groups circumvent the problem of combining an amoeboid mode of feeding with skeletal support and protection. In the next section, we examine more closely the various mechanisms of support and protection in protoctists.

Figure 2.8 (a) A foraminiferan *Polystomella crispa*; (b) A heliozoan actinopod *Actinophrys sol*.

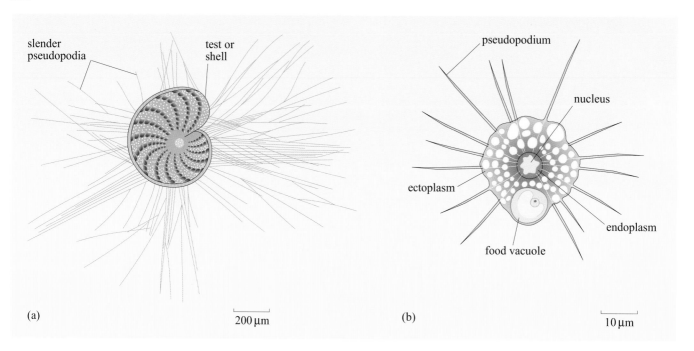

slender pseudopodia

test or shell

pseudopodium

nucleus

ectoplasm

endoplasm

food vacuole

(a)

200 μm

(b)

10 μm

SUMMARY OF SECTION 2.3

1 Osmotrophy and phagocytosis are the two main methods of feeding in heterotrophic protoctists.

2 Osmotrophy involves absorption of soluble organic molecules across the cell surface and, although it may supplement feeding in many species, is used exclusively only by internal parasites and by groups such as the oomycetes and slime nets which break down solid food by extracellular digestion before absorbing the soluble products. No special type of movement is required for osmotrophy.

3 Phagocytosis involves engulfment of food particles (endocytosis) and digestion within the cell inside food vacuoles. It requires a flexible cell surface which, in amoebae, occupies the whole surface. Amoebae feed and move by amoeboid movement using pseudopodia.

4 Other phagotrophs use flagella or cilia either to move towards prey or to create feeding currents. All have a definite shape which is produced by stiffening of the outer cytoplasm through development of the cytoskeleton. An unstiffened pocket (the gullet) may be used for phagocytic feeding.

5 Some later-evolved phyla (e.g. forams, actinopods) have lost flagella and become secondarily amoeboid but have rigid outer coverings. Their pseudopodia protrude through openings in the covering and are used for feeding, active swimming or walking.

2.4 PROTECTION AND SUPPORT

You have seen in Section 2.3 that the various methods of supporting and stiffening protoctist cells influence feeding and locomotion. In this section we examine more closely the nature of support and protection systems, the evolutionary pressures (selective forces) that led to their appearance and the diversity that resulted.

About 1000 Ma ago, during the Proterozoic era (2500–560 Ma), two changes occurred which are thought to have paved the way for the evolution of protection and support systems.

• The rise in atmospheric oxygen and the evolution of mitochondria from aerobic endosymbionts allowed protoctists to become aerobes, with a greatly increased supply of energy from their food. There was now plenty of energy to synthesize new kinds of large complex molecules.

• A structure evolved (not present in the Archezoa) that allowed secretion of complex carbohydrates, proteins and the linking together of carbohydrate and protein to make glycoproteins. This structure is called the **Golgi apparatus**.

Coupled with the increasing complexity of the cytoskeleton and a more complex system of internal membranes, the Golgi apparatus allowed cells to secrete external structures such as scales, and materials that form hairs and cell walls. The fossil record shows that during the middle and late Proterozoic there was an increase in size, complexity and numbers of protoctists with tough, resistant coverings. Most appear to be resting stages or *cysts* but of what is still uncertain.

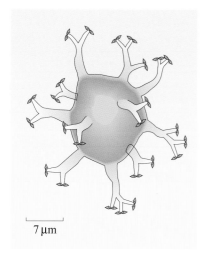

7 μm

Figure 2.9 A fossilized protoctistan cyst, similar to those found in the Proterozoic.

Some look like early forms of unicellular green algae; others like dinoflagellate cysts; and in the late 1990s fossils of multicellular algae — red, green and brown (phyla 6, 12 and 22, respectively) with cell walls were discovered in China, alongside the animal embryo fossils described in Chapter 1 (Section 1.5.4). The cyst coverings probably gave some protection against the elements (desiccation and UV radiation, for example) but the elaborate surface sculpting of some (Figure 2.9) suggests that *protection against being eaten* could also have been important. Most of the protoctistan cysts disappeared from the fossil record at the end of Proterozoic, a period when there was much tectonic activity and geological upheaval. But a whole array of more complex protected forms evolved during the following Cambrian era, together with the radiation of early animals described in Chapter 1.

Cell skeletons in protoctists have other functions besides protection, however, and we consider three of them before examining further the diversification that occurred in the Cambrian and beyond.

(I) MAINTAINING CELL SHAPE

There are often advantages for protoctists in having a definite shape. For all the actively swimming species, the 'optimal' shape depends on size, habitat and the relative importance of fast or strong swimming. Even for attached phagocytic protoctists (e.g Figure 2.6b and c), shape may have a crucial influence on feeding currents and prey capture. In the large, multicellular algae, including the brown and red seaweeds, cell shape becomes important because it affects the way that cells pack together to form tissues.

(II) FLOTATION

Planktonic protoctists, i.e. those that live in the water column rather than on surfaces, often need to maintain a particular position, for example, in the well-lit surface water for autotrophs or in areas of high prey density for heterotrophs. The problem is how to do so. Large cells may be able to maintain position by active swimming but non-motile cells inevitably tend to sink, especially if they have heavy outer coverings, as diatoms (algae in phylum 24) do. One way of reducing the rate of sinking is to have a spread-out shape and some diatoms achieve this by grouping cells together (Figure 2.10). Others, particularly the actinopods (phylum 27), have elaborate projections or lattices made of rigid, skeletal material (Figure 2.11) as well as stiffened projecting pseudopodia (Figure 2.8b). The shapes of cells or groups of cells, which depend on the cell skeleton, can thus influence flotation.

(III) CELL SIZE

Shapeless, shell-less amoebas can be relatively large (the archamoeban *Pelomyxa palustris* may exceed 1 mm in diameter, for example) but for all protoctists with a definite shape, maximum cell size seems to depend on the amount of cell support. The support may be internal, by elaborate cytoskeletal structures, or it may involve external walls. In the ciliates (Ciliophora, phylum 10), for example, cells retain a flexible surface but can be quite large by virtue of an elaborate cytoskeletal underpinning, which acts also to control the beating of their

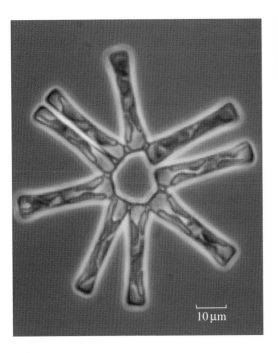

Figure 2.10 A star-shaped colony of the diatom *Asterionella formosa*. Cells grouped in this way sink more slowly than do single cells.

10 μm

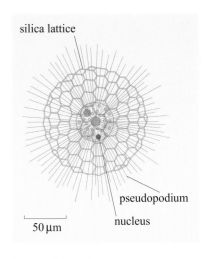

silica lattice

pseudopodium

nucleus

50 μm

Figure 2.11 *Heliosphaera*, an actinopod, showing the outer silica lattice with projecting pseudopodia.

numerous cilia. In the green algae (Chlorophyta, phylum 12), walled cells some hundreds of μm long occur in many groups with the prize for cell size going to the unicellular *Acetabularia* and near relatives: these attached cells whose wall is encrusted with calcium carbonate (lime) can be over 1 cm long (Figure 2.12).

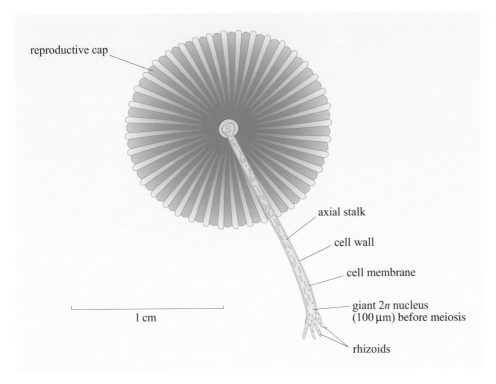

reproductive cap

axial stalk

cell wall

cell membrane

giant 2*n* nucleus (100 μm) before meiosis

rhizoids

1 cm

Figure 2.12 *Acetabularia* sp. (Chlorophyta), comprising a single giant cell.

So cell skeletons may provide protection, determine cell shape and influence flotation and cell size. Now consider the nature of these skeletons in more detail. Following on from the simple stiffening of outer cytoplasm seen in archezoan flagellates, two general types of cell skeleton evolved, both requiring secretion from the Golgi apparatus:

- those secreted *outside* the outer cell membrane and either completely enclosing the cell (**cell walls**) or partially enclosing it (*shells* or **tests**);

- those secreted *inside* the cell membrane, which have no common names and will be referred to as **endoskeletons** (meaning intracellular in the context of protoctists). They should not be confused with the cytoskeleton.

Endoskeletons probably evolved first and one of the simplest types is seen in the euglenoid algae (phylum 4), where flat strips of protein form a layer just below the cell membrane (Figure 2.13a). This layer is relatively flexible so that, although swimming euglenoids maintain their shape, many can contract, stretch and squirm about when on a solid surface. A later evolutionary development is seen in the dinoflagellates (phylum 9), which have a close-fitting armour

Figure 2.13 Endoskeletons in (a) *Euglena*; the diagonal bands are protein strips that form a flexible layer, the pellicle. (b) A dinoflagellate *Ceratium* showing the cellulose plates which are enclosed in vesicles below the cell membrane.

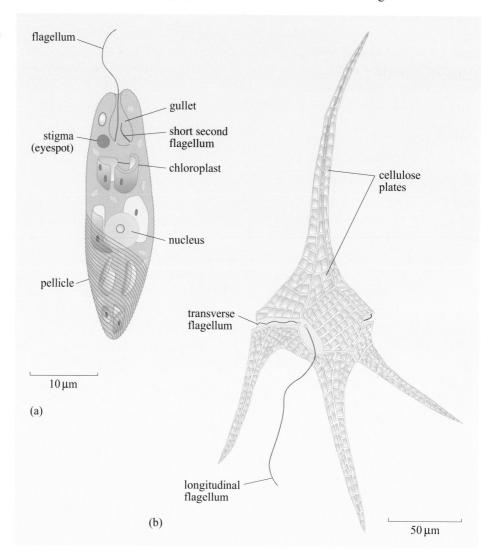

flagellum

gullet

stigma (eyespot)

short second flagellum

chloroplast

nucleus

pellicle

cellulose plates

transverse flagellum

longitudinal flagellum

10 μm

(a)

(b)

50 μm

consisting of cellulose plates formed below the cell membrane (Figure 2.13b). The plates may be further strengthened by deposition of silica or calcium carbonate and generate an amazing variety of cell shapes that are often used as a basis for classifying species. The endoskeleton becomes even more complex in the actinopods as illustrated earlier in Figure 2.11 and this phylum includes some very large and strikingly beautiful unicellular protoctists.

Cell walls and tests evolved independently in several protoctist phyla. Cell walls in the broadest sense are *any rigid structures which completely surround the cell(s) and are intimately connected to the cell*; they occur in nearly all the later-evolved autotrophs (i.e. the algae) and are universal in multicellular algae.

○ Would you expect to find cell walls in any heterotrophic protoctists?

● No, because the all-enclosing wall prevents phagocytic feeding. The only exception which you might have thought of are the fungus look-alikes, the oomycetes (phylum 19) which have cellulose walls and feed osmotrophically after extracellular digestion (Section 2.3).

The organic components of cell walls are typically (e.g. in the red, green and brown algae) of two types: a tough fibrillose material (usually cellulose) and a glue-like matrix that holds the fibres together. The matrix material can be extracted to produce agar which is widely used in the food and pharmaceutical industries, for example in the manufacture of ice-cream, jam, ointments and toothpaste. Additional protection is obtained in some algae by **calcification**— secretion into the wall or deposition from the outside water of calcium carbonate, $CaCO_3$ (Figure 2.14). Calcified red algae may occur as a hard encrusting layer on sea-shore rocks and play an important role in cementing together the coral colonies of coral reefs.

Diatoms (Figure 2.10) and a few other algae strengthen their walls with *silica*, the mineral of which quartz (sand) is composed. The intricate, lace-like structure of diatom walls (Figure 2.15) is the main character used to classify this group of algae.

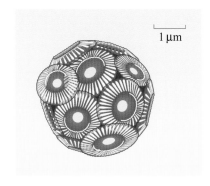

1 μm

Figure 2.14 *Emiliania huxleyi*, a minute coccolithophorid (Haptophyta, phylum 15) showing the calcified scales that cover its surface. These scales are formed inside the Golgi apparatus and secreted whole onto the surface.

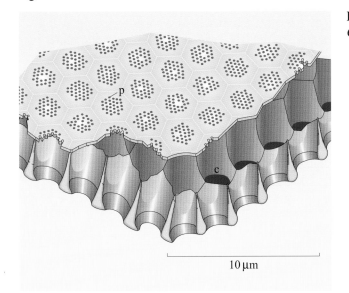

10 μm

Figure 2.15 Cross-section of a two-layered wall of the diatom *Coscinodiscus* showing the pores (p) and internal chambers (c).

In contrast to cell walls, the shells or tests of protoctists do not enclose cells completely, so that pseudopodia can be extruded and phagocytic feeding remains possible. The shells of forams (Figure 2.8), the cellulose armour plating of dinoflagellates (Figure 2.13b) and the cases of tintinnid ciliates (Figure 2.7c) are examples and all have evolved convergently in different phyla. The structures may be produced in various ways but, for example, the foram tests are commonly formed by precipitating calcium carbonate onto an organic template. In free-swimming forams from shallow water the strength of tests, determined by shape and thickness, increases with cell size and water turbulence, supporting the view that tests have a primary protective role.

MINERALIZATION

From the discussion above you can see that strengthening of protoctist skeletons, both internal and external, often involves deposition of inorganic (mineral) material. Mineralization is widespread in the animal kingdom, vertebrate bone and the calcareous skeletons of corals being obvious examples, but only in protoctists does it become a process of global significance. There are two main reasons for this assertion.

1   The *effect on the carbon cycle*. When the skeletal remains of marine calcareous protoctists sink into deep water they 'lock up', in the carbonate anion, significant amounts of carbon. The result is similar if large numbers of heavy living cells (such as diatoms) sink and remain undecomposed on the sea bed. Removal of carbon from the water column means that more CO_2 can dissolve into the oceans from the atmosphere, and so influence atmospheric concentrations of CO_2 and the global cycling of carbon.

2   Over geological time mineralized skeletons and shells can form vast deposits on the sea bed and heat and pressure may change (metamorphose) the deposits into sedimentary rocks. The pyramids of Egypt are composed of limestone produced largely from foram tests; coccolithophorids (phylum 15) have contributed greatly to chalk; and both diatom walls (phylum 24) and actinopod skeletons (phylum 27), are major components of silica-rich marine oozes. Palaeontologists use such skeletal remains of protoctists (and of invertebrate animals) to date sedimentary rocks and cores of sediment and, more importantly, to detect major events, such as mass extinctions, and changes of climate or other environmental conditions. This is the science of *biostratigraphy*.

SUMMARY OF SECTION 2.4

1   During the Proterozoic, two factors probably facilitated the evolution of rigid outer coverings in protoctists: (i) the rise in atmospheric oxygen plus aerobic metabolism ensured adequate supplies of energy for biosynthesis; and (ii) evolution of the Golgi apparatus plus further elaboration of the cytoskeleton and internal membranes allowed the synthesis and secretion of structural materials.

2   External structures (cell walls and tests) can protect cells against environmental hazards or predation. Both external and internal support structures may help to maintain cell shape, promote flotation and influence maximum cell size.

3 Endoskeletons range from flexible strips of protein (euglenoids), to hefty plates of cellulose (dinoflagellates), to elaborate cage-like structures (actinopods). Both of the last two structures may be mineralized.

4 Cell walls that enclose the cell totally occur mainly in autotrophs (algae) and preclude phagocytic feeding. They are composed of organic materials secreted by the cell but may be further strengthened by mineralization (e.g. calcification or (in diatoms) deposition of silica). As shells or tests do not enclose the cell completely they do not preclude phagocytic feeding. They appear to be mainly protective.

5 Mineralization of both internal and external cell skeletons in protoctists has had major, long-term effects on the environment: (a) by sequestering carbon in the deep sea as calcified skeletons, there is an effect on the global carbon cycle; (b) sedimentary rocks such as chalk and limestone are composed of metamorphosed skeletal deposits.

2.5 MULTICELLULARITY, SIZE AND SHAPE

Animals, plants and true fungi — the so-called higher eukaryote kingdoms — are all multicellular organisms, but very few prokaryotes and only three groups of algae in the protoctists have reached this level of organization. Why is there such a sharp distinction between the 'lower' and 'higher' organisms in this respect? What are the advantages of having many cells rather than one cell? To try and answer these questions we consider first the implications of *size* and how multicellularity is one way of increasing size that has profound implications for shape and the ways in which organisms function.

2.5.1 SIZE—GETTING BIGGER

When there is strong competition for limiting resources such as light (for autotrophs), or attachment sites or food (for heterotrophs), then natural selection for increase in size often occurs. Predation by small filter-feeding animals may also lead to selection for larger cell size in protoctists — big ones are less likely to be eaten. Larger cells can be less dense and more buoyant, which may be advantageous for free-floating protoctists. For reasons we cannot explain here, they also use less energy per unit volume than do smaller cells and so may be better able to survive brief periods of nutrient shortage. However, there are strong constraints on the size of a single cell, one of which relates to the supply of essential materials, whether gases, organic molecules or ions, and to the removal of waste materials.

○ This point was first raised in connection with osmotrophic feeding (Section 2.3.1). What ratio influences most strongly the supply of materials to the centre of a roughly spherical cell?

● The ratio of surface area to volume ($S:V$).

We explore this relationship more fully here. For a sphere, the surface area is proportional to the square of the radius and the volume to the cube of the radius.

○ If a spherical cell of radius r doubles its radius to $2r$, what is the relative change in (a) the surface area, (b) the volume and (c) the ratio $S{:}V$?

● For the cell of radius r, surface area and volume are related to r^2 and r^3, respectively. With a radius of $2r$, the comparable values are $(2r)^2$ and $(2r)^3$, i.e. $4r^2$ and $8r^3$. So, (a) surface area increases by a factor of 4, (b) volume increases by a factor of 8 and (c) the ratio $S{:}V$ falls by a factor of $4/8 = 0.5$, i.e. it is halved.

So we have a situation where doubling the radius of a cell increases the volume and the materials required to support metabolism by eightfold but halves the $S{:}V$ ratio. Only if the *supply* of essential materials (e.g. oxygen) increased 16-fold would the cell continue exactly as before when the radius was r. Such an increase in supply rate is usually impossible because materials move from the outside to the inside of a cell by *diffusion*, a process which should be familiar from earlier studies. Because it depends on the random movements of molecules, diffusion is a *very* slow process, especially in a fluid. Gases diffuse 10 000 times more slowly through water than through air. Furthermore, large molecules diffuse more slowly than small ones and the time taken for a molecule to diffuse from a point source is proportional to the square of the distance travelled: if it takes one second to move distance x, it takes four seconds to move a distance $2x$ (time being proportional to 2^2) and 100 s to move distance $10x$. The full equation for time required for diffusion includes a term (the diffusion coefficient) that varies with molecular size and the question below asks you to use this equation to calculate real times for diffusion of glucose.

○ Time required for diffusion is given by the equation:

$$\text{time } (t) = \frac{\text{distance}^2}{\text{diffusion coefficient } (D)} \times \text{constant (K)}$$

For glucose molecules, D is approximately $10^{-9}\,\text{m}^2\,\text{s}^{-1}$ so, using a value of one for K (which depends on the shape of the system), calculate how long it would take glucose molecules to diffuse (a) 1 μm (b) 10 mm (c) 1 m. Hint: make sure that you use the same units of distance for the top and bottom lines.

● (a) 1 μm $= 10^{-6}$ m so $t = [(10^{-6}\,\text{m})^2/(10^{-9}\,\text{m}^2\,\text{s}^{-1})] \times 1 = 10^{-12}/10^{-9} = 10^{-3}$ s. (b) 10^5 s (multiplying the answer to (a) by $(10\,000)^2) = 1.16$ days. (c) 10^9 s, which is 32 years!

Cell size is, therefore, constrained by the problem of *supplying materials to the centre of the cell by diffusion from outside*. A surprisingly large number of mostly autotrophic protoctists in the oceans, where the environment is relatively constant and predation pressure low, have avoided the diffusion problem by remaining small or becoming even smaller. The smallest cells are thought to have evolved from larger cells. These minute plankton have no problems with diffusional supply and effectively mimic bacteria.

Among larger protoctists, however, there are ways round this supply problem, one of which is illustrated in Figure 2.16.

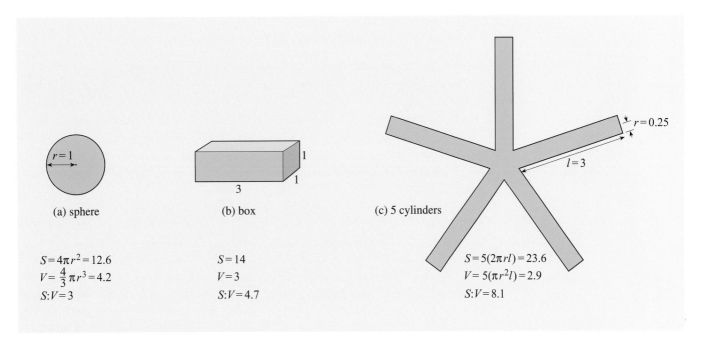

(a) sphere (b) box (c) 5 cylinders

$S = 4\pi r^2 = 12.6$ $S = 14$ $S = 5(2\pi rl) = 23.6$
$V = \frac{4}{3}\pi r^3 = 4.2$ $V = 3$ $V = 5(\pi r^2 l) = 2.9$
$S{:}V = 3$ $S{:}V = 4.7$ $S{:}V = 8.1$

○ From Figure 2.16, identify one way round the diffusional supply problem.

● As cells get bigger a relatively high $S{:}V$ ratio can be maintained if cells have a flattened or lobed shape, rather than being spherical.

Figure 2.16 Three cells of similar volume but differing in the ratio $S{:}V$ because of their different shapes.

Among protoctists, larger cells are indeed often *flattened* or *lobed*. A second way round the problem is to have *active streaming movements of cell cytoplasm* — a sort of internal circulation — so that materials taken up at the cell surface are carried rapidly to the cell interior. Such movement is seen in, for example, many actinopods (phylum 27, Figure 2.8b), where cytoplasmic streaming occurs up and down the slender pseudopodia (Section 2.3.2), and in the giant cells of some green algae (e.g. *Acetabularia*, Figure 2.12); it is also common in the cells of plants and in the axons of animal nerve cells. Large cells in some algae (and plants) have a third way round the problem: 90% of the centre of the cell may be occupied by one or more **vacuoles**, which are membrane-bound sacs containing mainly small molecules but none of the cell machinery that requires large supplies of energy. You can think of vacuoles as a sort of metabolic dead space but useful for storage.

A combination of change in cell shape, cytoplasmic streaming and vacuoles can, therefore, overcome some of the constraints on cell size imposed by diffusion. But these mechanisms cannot easily overcome a second constraint on cell size: that imposed by the problem of *information transfer, co-ordination and control*. The main information store in a cell is its nuclear DNA and in order to respond to external signals (by making new enzymes, for example), information is transferred from nucleus to cytoplasm as messenger RNA and used to direct the synthesis of new (or more) enzymes. As cell size increases, it becomes increasingly difficult for information to reach the nucleus rapidly and to move from nucleus to distant cytoplasm fast enough to make a rapid, co-ordinated response.

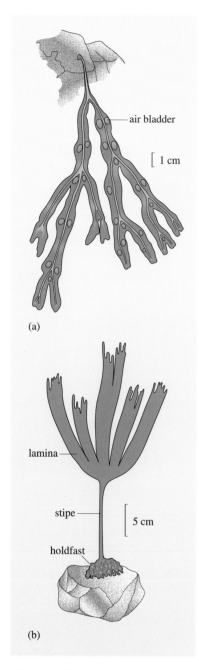

Figure 2.18 Brown seaweeds (phylum 22, Phaeophyta). (a) Bladderwrack, *Fucus vesiculosus*; (b) a kelp or oarweed, *Laminaria digitata*.

○ A partial solution to this problem of information transfer is illustrated in Figure 2.12 (*Acetabularia*); what is the solution?

● The nucleus has become greatly enlarged. It is labelled 'giant nucleus' in Figure 2.12.

What you cannot see on this figure but is revealed by electron microscopy and experiments is that the nucleus is extremely active with huge numbers of pores in the nuclear envelope and much RNA synthesis. Other protoctists in which cells for at least one stage in the life cycle attain a large size (several mm or cm) have *many nuclei per cell* (oomycetes and the myxomycetes (non-cellular slime moulds), for example). The term used to describe the naked (i.e. wall-less) multinucleate mass of cytoplasm in myxomycetes, which looks like a pulsating layer of slime, is **plasmodium**. Ciliates (phylum 10) have evolved a system whereby the *amount of DNA per chromosome* is increased. In fact this greatly oversimplifies the situation in ciliates which have two sorts of nuclei: a large macronucleus in which chromosomes break up into fragments (some of which are then destroyed) and the DNA in the remaining fragment replicates many times; and a small micronucleus with one complete set of genetic material and about one-fortieth as much DNA as the macronucleus (Figure 2.17). All the RNA synthesis necessary to maintain ciliate cells is carried out by the macronucleus while the micronucleus does nothing except take part in sexual reproduction!

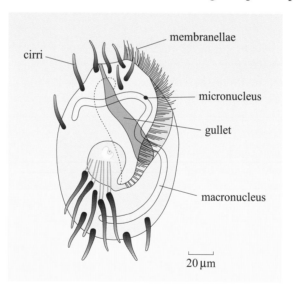

Figure 2.17 *Euplotes*, a ciliate, showing the large, metabolically active macronucleus (which does not undergo meiosis) and the small micronucleus which undergoes meiosis and is involved only in reproduction.

The largest protoctists, however, achieve a large size by increasing the number of *cells*: they are multicellular or colonial.

2.5.2 MULTICELLULARITY

Most of the really large protoctists are multicellular algae, the biggest being seaweeds that grow on rocky shores or in shallow coastal water (Figure 2.18): giant kelps (brown algae) growing off the coast of northwest America, can be up to 50 m in length. In such habitats the selective pressures for large size are clear. Water turbulence means that algae can persist only if they are *anchored* and, once anchored, they can reach the light (when underwater) and shade out competitors only by getting bigger.

The question remains as to how multicellularity overcomes the constraints imposed by diffusion of essential molecules and information transfer, discussed above for single cells. In multicellular organisms, cells, each with their own nucleus, can remain small so that the problem of information transfer *within* cells is avoided. The solution to the problem of co-ordinating the whole multicellular organism and of maintaining essential supplies to all parts depends largely on *cell specialization*: when there are many cells, some can become specialized or **differentiate** to perform particular functions.

Laminaria hyperborea (Figure 2.19), a brown alga and one of the perennial kelps found on British shores, can be used to illustrate this important concept.

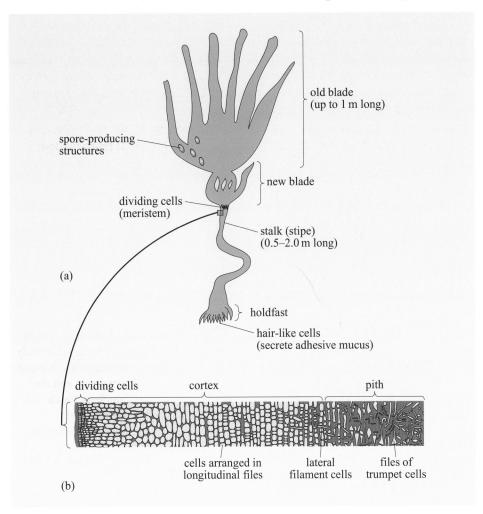

Figure 2.19 *Laminaria hyperborea*, a kelp (brown seaweed). (a) The whole alga; (b) vertical section of the upper part of the stalk or stipe.

○ From Figure 2.19 what evidence can you see for cell differentiation?

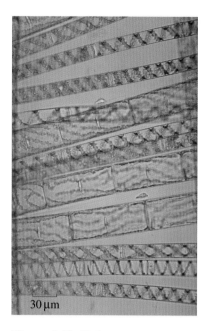

30 μm

Figure 2.20 Unbranched filaments consisting of chains of cells in the green alga *Spirogyra* sp., which is found mainly in still fresh water. The spiral structures are chloroplasts.

● Specialized mucus-producing hair-like cells occur on the holdfast (which attaches the kelp to rocks) and the spore-producing structures must contain cells specialized for reproduction. In Figure 2.19b, different tissues containing cells of different shapes and sizes from the top of the stalk are shown.

All these cells perform particular functions. For example, the dividing cells are responsible for growth and the trumpet cells in the pith of the stalk are involved in the transport of materials from the photosynthetic blade to the largely non-photosynthetic stalk. Blade cells are specialized to perform photosynthesis whereas stalk cells do not photosynthesize and depend on the blade for supplies of sugars. There are close parallels with plants. However, the specialized cells and tissues that are required to coordinate a mobile animal (nerve cells and muscle, for example) are absent and there are no equivalents in the protoctists. Specialized systems for long-distance transport are the main way in which complex multicellular organisms circumvent the problem of diffusional supply and animals and plants have evolved very elaborate systems compared with the simple systems in algae. Movement in cells such as trumpet cells (Figure 2.19b) involves *mass flow*, as happens when liquid is sucked up or blown through a straw, which is many times faster than diffusion. It would take years for sugars produced at the top of a giant kelp blade to reach the non-photosynthetic cells near the base of the stalk by diffusion, but only 2–3 days via the trumpet cell system.

Other supply problems are solved by the shape of algae. For example, photosynthetic cells must be supplied with carbon dioxide (or HCO_3^- ions) by diffusion from the outside and cannot, therefore, be separated from the outside by more than a few layers of cells. Hence the photosynthetic parts of seaweeds tend to be thread-like or strongly flattened (as in *L. hyperborea*, Figure 2.19). In fresh water the majority of multicellular algae are Chlorophyta (green algae, phylum 12) and most consist of simple, delicate filaments (Figure 2.20).

Chains of single cells are the simplest structures that can be called multicellular but they may still show some degree of cell specialization. Another level of cell organization in protoctists does not go as far and is intermediate between unicellular and multicellular states — colonial organization.

2.5.3 COLONIAL PROTOCTISTS

A widely used definition of a **colony** is that it is an association of individual organisms that are linked together either by living extensions of their bodies (e.g. cytoplasmic strands) or by non-living material that they have secreted. This definition is rather imprecise but implies that although there may be communication between members of a colony, there is little or no cell differentiation: all individuals in a colony are functionally equivalent and could survive and form a new colony if isolated. Figure 2.21 shows some examples of colonial protoctists.

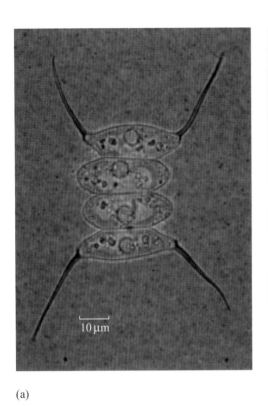

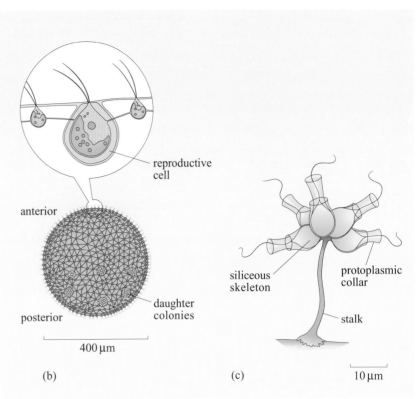

(a)

(b)

(c)

○ (a) How are the cells linked together in the three colonies shown in Figure 2.21? (b) Is there any evidence that cells are *not* all functionally equivalent in any of the three examples?

● (a) In *Scenedesmus* they appear to be simply in close physical contact; in *Volvox* cells embedded in mucus are linked by cytoplasmic strands; and in *Codosiga* cells are joined by the siliceous skeleton. (b) Yes, in *Scenedesmus* the outer two cells of the colony have slender processes. Also, in *Volvox*, where it is stated in the legend that daughter colonies form only from particular large cells. Notice also that the colonies have polarity, with a front end (that leads the way when moving) and a rear end (where most of the daughter colonies occur). These features also suggest some degree of cell specialization in the colony and some biologists do indeed regard *Volvox* as having reached a multicellular grade.

Figure 2.21 Colonial protoctists. (a) *Scenedesmus* sp., a green alga with four-celled colonies. (b) *Volvox* sp. a green alga with up to several thousand cells lying over the surface of a ball of mucus. The dark spots are daughter colonies which develop inside the surface layer by division of certain large cells. Individual cells with two flagella and linked by cytoplasmic strands are shown above. (c) *Codosiga* sp., a colonial choanoflagellate (phylum 28).

Clearly, the boundary between a multicellular and a colonial protoctist is not always sharp. The crucial question is whether any cells become so specialized (e.g. for reproduction, transport or defence) that they have to be supplied with nutrients by other cells. Overall, colonial living can be regarded as a mechanism that allows protoctists to achieve some increase in size but with individual cells maintaining a higher degree of independence than in multicellular types. It is a relatively small innovation but recall that animals are thought to have evolved from choanoflagellates (Chapter 1) and so the colonial stage can be regarded as a step on the way to multicellularity.

SUMMARY OF SECTION 2.5

1   There may be selection for larger cell size in protoctists through competition for limiting resources, predation or the need for flotation. However, maximum size of spherical cells is constrained by problems of: (i) supplying materials to the cell interior by diffusion from the outside; (ii) transferring information from and to the nucleus and co-ordinating and controlling the cell.

2   The supply problem in unicells, (i), may be solved by evolving a flattened or lobed shape (maintaining a high ratio of $S:V$); cytoplasmic streaming; and vacuoles.

3   The information transfer problem in unicells, (ii), may be solved by having a single but large and very active nucleus (e.g. *Acetabularia*); becoming multinucleate; or having large amounts of active DNA (as in the macronucleus of ciliates).

4   In three autotrophic phyla, the green, red and brown algae, large size has been achieved by becoming multicellular and differentiating specialized cells and tissues. Supply problems are solved by having a flattened or filamentous shape and cells specialized for long-distance transport.

5   Colonial protoctists achieve a modest increase in size by grouping cells together but without the differentiation of specialized cells and tissues characteristic of multicellular organisms.

2.6   AN OVERVIEW OF PROTOCTIST DIVERSITY: SEX, LIFE CYCLES AND SYMBIOSIS

In the last four sections we considered four types of innovation that have allowed protoctists to exploit new habitats, compete more effectively and adapt to a wide range of conditions, in sum, to diversify. Many of the innovations are unique to protoctists, for example the acquisition of mitochondria, chloroplasts, flagella and a cytoskeleton. Such features were available to the three kingdoms that evolved from protoctists and were neither innovations in these kingdoms nor a primary cause of their diversification. In this last section we consider three topics which are just as important for the diversification of other eukaryote kingdoms as they are for protoctists. The topics are sexual reproduction, life cycles and symbiosis. They are considered here partly to pave the way for later discussions and partly to complete the story of protoctist diversification, in which all three processes played a major role.

2.6.1   SEXUAL REPRODUCTION

You can see in Figure 2.1 that sexual reproduction is thought to have evolved about 1500 Ma ago, relatively early in protoctist evolution. It was immediately followed by the protoctist 'big bang' — a period of rapid diversification for which evidence derives largely from fossils, especially types that had resistant cell walls or skeletons. The conjunction of sexual reproduction and rapid diversification is probably significant.

○ From your knowledge of sexual reproduction from earlier studies, suggest why it might lead to greater diversification.

● By producing new combinations of genes in gametes (at meiosis) and bringing gametes together (at fertilization or cell fusion), sexual reproduction generates new genotypes which, if favoured by natural selection, can give rise to new types of organisms.

There is certainly some truth in this idea and the near-universality of sexual reproduction in animals and plants attests to its value. As in mitosis, slightly different versions of meiosis and sexual reproduction appear to have evolved independently in different protoctist lineages, including all those with large cells (e.g. ciliates (phylum 10) and the multicellular algae). We can reasonably assume that sexual reproduction has played a part in the evolution and diversification of these lineages. But there are other protoctist lineages in which there is no evidence of sexual reproduction and either it does not occur or is so rare that it has never been observed. The euglenoid algae, for example (Figure 2.13a, phylum 4) have been cultured and observed closely for over 50 years with no evidence of sexual reproduction and perhaps the process never evolved in these organisms.

○ Suggest another explanation for the absence of sexual reproduction in a protoctist lineage.

● The process may have been secondarily *lost*. There is no way of knowing for certain but the balance of opinion among algal experts is that euglenoids have never had sexual reproduction.

Secondary loss of sex or modification of the process so that new genetic combinations are not produced has certainly occurred in animals, plants and fungi, all of which points to the conclusion that there must be *disadvantages* of sexual reproduction: in certain organisms in certain conditions, the disadvantages can outweigh the advantages. A point we want to emphasize here is that some protoctist lineages quite possibly evolved and diversified *without* sexual reproduction.

2.6.2 LIFE CYCLES

When thinking about diversity in protoctists or any other type of organism the focus is usually on the mature organism, the stage of the life cycle that feeds (or photosynthesizes) and reproduces. Such a focus is reasonable for most vertebrate animals but for many other organisms, including many protoctists, it is not justifiable because different stages in the life cycle may be adapted to different conditions and look or function quite differently. Diversity, therefore, exists *within* life cycles. In addition, the general types of life cycle may differ with respect to the ploidy (haploid or diploid) of the dominant stages, as you saw in Chapter 1 for plants, where a haploid stage dominates in bryophytes but a diploid stage dominates in vascular plants. Both of these important concepts are well illustrated in protoctists and are discussed below; protoctists show more diversity of life cycles than any other kingdom. First, however, we need to think more carefully about what a life cycle is.

DEFINITION OF A LIFE CYCLE

For multicellular organisms such as human beings the life cycle can be simply defined as *the sequence of changes from origin (zygote) to death* with adults producing young to complete the cycle and start a new one (Figure 2.22a). Any changes that occur are within a single individual and in a single generation. In unicellular organisms, however, a new individual and generation is created every time a cell divides, which can occur hundreds or thousands of times during a life cycle. Many individuals originate and die during such a life cycle so a new definition of life cycle is required: *the sequence of changes necessary for an organism to persist and attain a particular form in a given environment* is one definition. There is no reference to individuals, origins or death and emphasis shifts to the environment. Figure 2.22b illustrates this concept of a life cycle as applied to a protoctist. Stages A and B each represent different sorts of individual, any of which may replicate many times. The same kind of life cycle but with different *multicellular* stages occurs in some invertebrate animals, notably certain internal parasites (such as flukes). A real example of such a life cycle in a protoctist (that of the malaria parasite) is described later and illustrated in Figure 2.23.

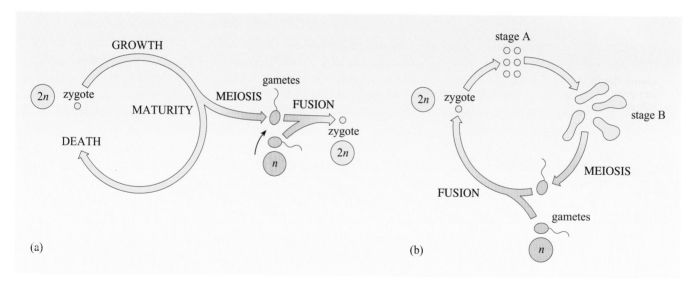

(a)

(b)

Figure 2.22 Generalized life cycles. (a) A multicellular diploid organism where all changes occur within one individual; (b) a unicellular diploid protoctist where each stage is represented by many individuals which may replicate.

Notice in Figure 2.22b that sexual reproduction occurs at only one stage in the life cycle and the zygote can be taken as the starting point (as in Figure 2.22a). Quite commonly, however, in both protoctists and other eukaryotic kingdoms (especially fungi), one stage in the sexual life cycle may act as the start and end point of a separate *asexual* cycle, examples of which are illustrated later in Figures 2.23 and 2.25. Organisms lacking sexual reproduction naturally have only asexual life cycles. The general point is that *an organism may have more than one type of life cycle* and which type predominates often depends on environmental conditions. If conditions are 'good', i.e. plenty of food/space/light or whatever an organism requires for growth and replication, the asexual cycle often dominates and the sexual cycle is reserved for less favourable conditions.

DIVERSITY WITHIN A LIFE CYCLE: THE MALARIA PARASITE

One of the most widespread infectious diseases of human beings is malaria, which kills more people than any other parasitic eukaryote, mainly in tropical countries. The agents which cause malaria are protoctists, *Plasmodium* spp. (phylum 11, Apicomplexa), whose life cycle provides a classic example in which there are several stages, each with a distinct morphology and function. It is illustrated in Figure 2.23.

Figure 2.23 Life cycle of a malarial parasite *Plasmodium vivax*. Purple indicates haploid stages and pink diploid stages. RBC = red blood cells.

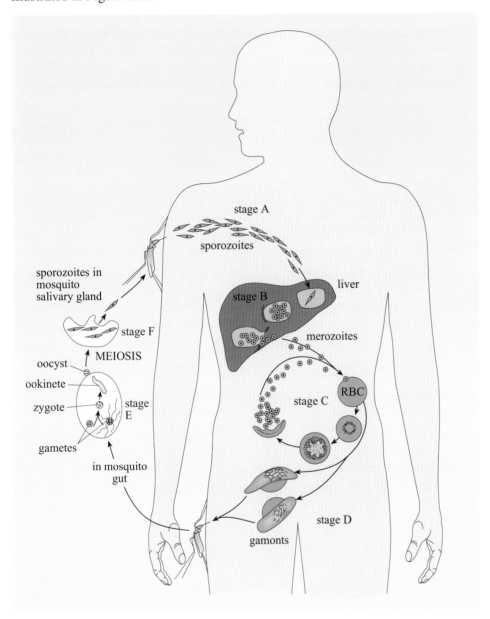

Notice that there are two hosts: human beings, where one stage of the life cycle occurs in liver cells and another in red blood cells; and a mosquito (*Anopheles* spp.). The mosquito picks up the parasite when it feeds on the blood of an infected person and transmits it in saliva after the parasite has passed from the gut to salivary glands.

○ Comparing Figure 2.23 with Figure 2.22b, there is one important difference relating to ploidy: what is it?

● In Figure 2.22b the organism is shown as diploid for stages A and B and meiosis is followed immediately by fusion. For *Plasmodium* in Figure 2.23, stages A to D are all haploid and fusion of gametes in the mosquito gut is followed shortly by meiosis. A predominantly haploid life cycle is more common in protoctists.

You can see in Figure 2.23 that at stages A and B *Plasmodium* undergoes repeated cycles of asexual reproduction which can be viewed as subsidiary 'loops' on the overall cycle. Each stage in this complex life cycle has a different name (which you are not expected to remember) and the notes below take you through the cycle step by step; you can also find out why malaria causes bouts of fever. Again, you are not expected to recall details of what happens at each stage but may be asked to use the notes as a reference source.

A–B   Initial infection of a human host is by haploid cells (sporozoites) that migrate first to the liver. Within liver cells the sporozoites grow, undergo mitosis and produce many small amoeboid cells which are released when the liver cells rupture and may either infect another liver cell (an asexual loop) or infect red blood cells (erythrocytes). The role of the liver stage appears to be production of a *Plasmodium* cell with the capacity to infect red blood cells.

C   Within red blood cells, *Plasmodium* undergoes a cycle similar to that occurring in the liver, i.e. growth (a feeding stage), mitosis and release of small infective cells by rupture of the host cell. This stage is generally regarded as the main feeding and growth stage by the osmotrophic parasites. It is also the stage that causes greatest damage to human hosts and produces the characteristic symptoms of malaria. Not only are blood cells destroyed, there is also a release of parasite toxins from the ruptured blood cells which causes malarial fever. The infective cells infect more blood cells and this asexual loop may be repeated many times. Parasites are released synchronously from all infected blood cells which results in the bouts of fever typical of malaria.

○ The fever caused by *Plasmodium vivax* returns every second day whereas that caused by another species, *P. malariae*, does so every three days. How can this difference be explained?

● The generation time for growth, cell division and synchronous release of infective cells must be two days in *P. vivax* but three days in *P. malariae*.

D   Eventually the infective cells differentiate into male and female gamonts (cells capable of producing gametes) which remain dormant within erythrocytes until sucked up by a mosquito, the secondary host.

E   Once the gamonts have entered a mosquito stomach, the female gamont differentiates into a large, spherical female gamete (equivalent to an egg cell) and the male gamont divides to release many small, flagellated male gametes, which fuse with the female gametes to form zygotes. Each zygote becomes an elongated ookinete which bores through the wall of the mosquito's stomach and becomes a thick-walled oocyst on the outside. Perhaps mosquitoes also feel ill at this stage.

F   The oocyst nucleus now undergoes meiosis and the products — small, spindle-shaped cells — divide further by mitosis until they are eventually set free into the blood of the mosquito where they migrate to the salivary gland. The cycle then starts all over again.

Similar sorts of life cycle occur in many protoctist parasites and the complexity relates mainly to the problem faced by a parasite in transmitting from one host to another. Such parasites are highly specialized and their life cycles raise many questions. How, for example, do parasites avoid the defensive immune responses of their hosts; and what signals trigger the different stages of the life cycle and direct parasite cells to particular host tissues?

LIFE CYCLES WITH DIFFERENT MULTICELLULAR STAGES IN ALGAE

All stages in the life cycle of *Plasmodium* are unicellular but in the large algal protoctists, there can be different *multicellular* stages. Plants have similar life cycles with alternation of generations as mentioned in Chapter 1 and the same terms are used to describe stages: the haploid gametophyte produces gametes by mitosis and the diploid sporophyte usually produces haploid spores after meiosis (see Figure 1.30 and following text).

Figure 2.24 illustrates the life cycle of the sea lettuce, *Ulva lactuca*, a green alga (phylum 12, Chlorophyta) that grows in rock pools and on sheltered shores around Britain.

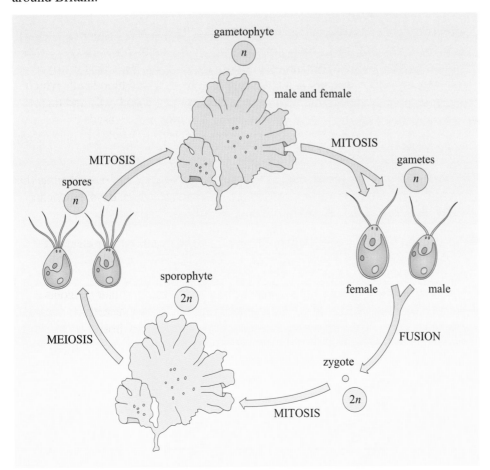

Figure 2.24 The life cycle of the green alga *Ulva lactuca,* the sea lettuce. Haploid stages are shown in purple and diploid stages in pink.

○ Is the algae you see the gametophyte or the sporophyte?

● It could be either: both stages (generations) in the life cycle are morphologically identical even though one is haploid and the other diploid.

Even the spores and gametes look similar except that the former have four flagella against two in the latter. Such morphological similarity of generations, spores and gametes is not found in plants. In other algae, however, the generations are not identical and this situation is illustrated in Figure 2.25 for the red alga *Porphyra tenera* (phylum 6, Rhodophyta). You do not need to remember details of this life cycle (although, for interest, some details are described in the legend to Figure 2.25) but note two points:

• The haploid generation (A) is dominant and is the familiar form that people refer to as *Porphyra*. It looks like a frilly red lettuce and grows on rocks in Japan in winter. The sporophyte generation (C) has a quite different, filamentous structure. It settles on and bores into mollusc shells where it is protected from desiccation and can persist for several years (in contrast to the gametophyte which dies off in summer). The sporophyte was actually classified as a separate species, *Conchocelis rosea*, before being identified as a generation of *Porphyra*.

• The gametophyte can produce asexual spores which grow into new gametophytes after settling, so here is another example of an asexual 'loop', a second type of life cycle in one organism.

Finding out about this life cycle has been of considerable economic value because *Porphyra* is a much-valued food in the far East. It was cultivated in Japan since the 17th century, simply by sticking bamboo canes into the sediment of sheltered bays and allowing spores to settle and grow into gametophytes. Since discovery of the sporophyte stage, production has been much increased by growing this phase on oyster shells which are then placed close to nets on which spores can settle. Having morphologically distinct, independent generations in a life cycle greatly increases protoctist diversity.

Among protoctists only certain red, green and brown algae (phyla 6, 12 and 22, respectively) show an alternation of multicellular generations and, although the life cycles differ in detail, they appear fundamentally similar.

○ Are these life cycles, therefore, analogous or homologous characters?

● Analogous: homologous characters would derive from a common ancestor in which those characters were present (Chapter 1).

Analogy suggests that there are strong selective forces acting on large algae which favour the evolution of alternating generations — but the nature of these selective forces is unclear. What is the advantage of having two sorts of mature individual in a life cycle? It is believed, because of other differences between algae in these phyla and because the multicellular types must have evolved from unicellular forms, that similarities in life cycles have arisen through *convergent evolution*. Comparative studies between early-evolved and later-evolved algae in

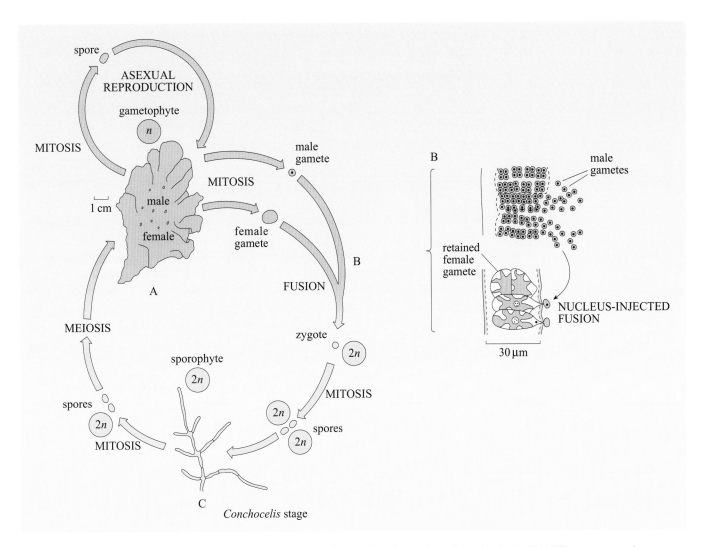

Figure 2.25 The life cycle of a red alga, *Porphyra tenera*, illustrating alternation of morphologically different generations. Haploid stages are shown in purple and diploid in pink. For stage B small, non-flagellated male gametes are released into the water from the gametophyte thallus but the large female gametes are retained in the thallus and fertilized only after a male gamete (from the same or a different thallus) settles on the surface and injects its nucleus into the egg cell. The diploid zygote (still in the gametophyte thallus) divides by mitosis and releases diploid spores which grow into a multicellular filamentous sporophyte. The sporophyte releases diploid spores and meiosis occurs only when a spore germinates; all four haploid cells produced then divide by mitosis and contribute to the gametophyte — the typical *Porphyra* thallus.

different groups suggest that the primitive life cycle was haplontic, i.e. only the zygote was diploid and meiosis followed immediately after fertilization. The trend, therefore, has been towards increasing emphasis on the diploid stage and, indeed, there are some brown algae (e.g. *Fucus* spp., the wracks which are common seaweeds) in which the diploid stage is totally dominant, just as it is in animals; the only haploid stage in these life cycles is the gametes. Even if this hypothesis is true, the question still remains as to why selection has favoured dominant diploids rather than haploids.

2.6.3 SYMBIOSIS AND PROTOCTIST DIVERSITY

Symbiosis means 'living together' of organisms, usually in some intimate association where there is close interaction, often at the cellular level. The importance of symbiosis in promoting diversification and shaping evolution cannot be overstated. We consider here only a few aspects of symbiosis that are relevant to protoctists, the main question being 'how has symbiosis influenced diversification in this kingdom?'

○ First, think back over this chapter and Chapter 1 and try to identify any interactions which you would classify as symbiotic.

● The most obvious examples are the interactions between Bacteria and early protoctists that gave rise to mitochondria and chloroplasts by endosymbiosis. Here the intracellular bacterium (the symbiont) was actually assimilated fully into the larger host cell; many bacterial genes were transferred to the host nucleus and the result was a loss of independence by the bacterial partner and the acquisition of whole suites of new metabolic properties by the host. The significance of these symbioses for protoctist evolution has already been discussed (Section 2.2) but the same kind of interaction has occurred repeatedly among protoctists (and other kingdoms) although without proceeding as far as total assimilation of the smaller partner. The general principle in most of these interactions is that a larger host protoctist takes into its cell a smaller symbiont (prokaryote or protoctist) which, instead of being eaten or killed, is *used* whilst alive as a source of new materials or properties. The most common type of interaction is that between heterotrophic protoctists (including forams, phylum 7, and ciliates, phylum 10) and algae.

○ What use do you think the algae are to the heterotrophs?

● They could act as a built-in food source by supplying photosynthetic products to the host, which would be useful if other sources of food were in short supply.

The alga in this sort of symbiosis has a protected habitat and may even be supplied with essential nutrients, such as phosphate, so the association could be described as **mutualistic**, meaning that both partners derive some benefit. Such terms are increasingly frowned upon, however, for two reasons:

(1) It is often impossible to tell what, if any, advantages the symbiont gains from the association and whether it is a mutualistic partner or a captive.

(2) Even if mutualism is established under one set of conditions it may not apply in others because symbiotic associations are dynamic and may change. A foram harbouring symbiotic algae, for example, may eject or consume the algae if external food sources become plentiful.

Such questions can only be resolved by experiments, for example isolating symbionts and observing how well they survive outside their host; or by comparing with untouched controls the performance of host cells after removal or destruction of their symbionts.

When asked earlier to identify symbiotic interactions you might also have thought of *Plasmodium* and malaria, i.e. **parasitism**. This too involves a close interaction between two organisms, but here the symbiont is the protoctist and it exploits the host as a source of food and as a habitat. Clearly, there is no benefit at all to the host in the malaria kind of symbiosis — quite the contrary — so that parasites tend to be regarded as agents of disease. In fact many parasites cause no detectable harm to their hosts and, in general, the longer a parasitic association exists, the less harm it tends to cause. There are indeed many associations, mainly involving ciliates or flagellates, where protoctists live in animal guts and appear to aid digestion.

○ What name could be given to this kind of symbiosis?

● Mutualism (if it was quite certain that both partners derived some benefit from the association).

For protoctists as symbionts, therefore, a complete spectrum exists from damaging parasites to useful mutualists. As external conditions change, the association may shift along the scale, so that a 'mutualist' becomes a 'parasite', exactly as described for the associations where protoctists act as hosts.

Parasitism is a very common way of life among protoctists. In phyla 11, 13, 14 and 26, for example, nearly all members are parasites of animal tissues whilst phylum 20 consists entirely of plant parasites. Each species of parasite tends to be highly specialized so that it can associate with only one or a small number of host species and with particular tissues or sites in the host. Such high degrees of specialization must have evolved from more general associations, for example with several host species or many tissues within one species. What probably happened is that different genetic strains of a generalized parasite became increasingly specialized to a particular host or tissue and hence increasingly isolated from other strains. The end result has been the evolution of many specialized parasites from a small number of generalists. So host specialization by parasites is a major cause of diversification within protoctists, as well as in Bacteria and animals. In contrast to the metabolic and structural innovations described in Sections 2.2–2.4, most of which occurred relatively early in protoctist evolution, diversification due to parasitism occurred relatively late because it depended on the evolution of plant and animal hosts.

SUMMARY OF SECTION 2.6

1   Sexual reproduction promotes the origin of new genotypes (through meiosis plus fusion between genetically different gametes) and is thought to have played a role in protoctist diversification, especially during the period of the 'big bang', 1300–1500 Ma ago. However, some ancient protoctist lineages appear never to have had sexual reproduction and in others it is extremely rare or secondarily absent.

2   Protoctists show great diversity both within their life cycles (having many functionally and morphologically different stages) and in the general types of cycle, particularly with respect to the ploidy of dominant stages.

3   A general definition of a life cycle applicable to protoctists is 'the sequence of changes necessary for an organism to persist in a given environment'. One species may have both sexual and asexual cycles, the latter often predominating when conditions are favourable for rapid growth and mitotic cell division.

4   The life cycle of the human malaria parasites, *Plasmodium* spp., is an example where a unicellular protoctist passes through several distinct stages with asexual loops occurring at two stages. A human and mosquito host are required and sexual reproduction occurs in the mosquito stomach. Meiosis rapidly follows cell fusion so that for most of its life cycle *Plasmodium* exists as haploid amoeboid cells.

5   Multicellular algae in the green, brown and red algal phyla have independently evolved life cycles with alternation of multicellular generations, as is found in plants. Such life cycles increase overall diversity. Comparative studies suggest that life cycles where the haploid gametophyte is dominant represent the primitive state and there has been an evolutionary trend towards increasing dominance of the diploid sporophyte.

6   Symbiosis has contributed greatly to diversification in protoctists, not only through the endosymbiotic origins of mitochondria and chloroplasts but also through many later interactions in which protoctists acted as host cells or evolved into specialized parasitic or mutualistic symbionts.

7   The most common symbiosis where the protoctist acts as host is between heterotrophs such as forams or ciliates and unicellular algae. The host acquires a food source (products of algal photosynthesis) and if there is some benefit to the algae, the association can be described as mutualistic. Often, however, it is impossible to determine the balance of advantage and, in any case, this balance may change as conditions change.

8   In parasitic and some mutualistic symbioses the protoctist is the symbiont and interacts with a larger host, usually an animal or plant. A parasite may cause severe damage to the host (disease) or have no detectable impact. Many highly specialized parasites confined to one host species and/or one sort of tissue have evolved from more generalized parasites. So specialization by parasites has contributed much to species diversity in protoctists.

FURTHER READING

Barnes, R.S.K. (ed.) (1998) *The Diversity of Living Organisms*, Blackwell Science, London.

Brusca, R. C. and Brusca, G. J. (1990) *Invertebrates*, Sinauer Associates Inc., Sunderland, Massachusetts.

Margulis, L. and Schwartz, K. V. (1998) (3rd edn) *Five Kingdoms: an illustrated guide to the phyla of life on Earth*, W. H. Freeman & Company, New York.

Van den Hoek, C., Mann, D. G. and Jahns, H. M. (1995) *Algae: an introduction to phycology*, Cambridge University Press, Cambridge. [An advanced textbook with detailed information about all algal groups.]

Biological investigation

3.1 Introduction

Like Earth sciences and astronomy, but in contrast to most branches of physics and chemistry, biology always has historical as well as contemporary dimensions: individuals have a life history, and species and populations must be understood in the contexts of their ancestry and evolutionary time. So as well as enquiring into situations and mechanisms as they are now, biologists are also interested in how the current state came into being, and what might happen to it in the future. There are common strategies for approaching different kinds of investigations, whether concerned with evolutionary origin, mechanism, function or interactions: nearly all kinds of scientific enquiry can be divided into three main components, theories, observations and experiments.

As indicated in the previous chapters, biologists have many kinds of questions, dealing with topics ranging from molecular structure to the size and composition of populations, and millions of species to which to address those questions. In spite of the diversity of species, many fundamental mechanisms of physiology and biochemistry are common to all or a large group of organisms and are therefore most conveniently investigated in species that happen to have features that suit them to particular research techniques. This chapter explains why certain species are chosen for this role, and the factors to be considered when concepts developed from them are extrapolated to other species that, for ethical as well as practical reasons, cannot be studied in the laboratory.

3.2 Hypotheses and theories

The essential feature of **theories** is that they integrate what is known into a rational scheme that can incorporate future discoveries of hitherto unknown information, whether further observations or experimental data. In the case of taxonomy, such new evidence may take the form of the discovery of a previously unknown species of fossil or living organisms, or new information about the structures or habitats of known ones. In the case of molecular biology, the new evidence may be another macromolecule that is isolated or a gene that is characterized; in the case of physiology or psychology, it may be results from a new kind of investigation, the use of more precise measurements or the study of comparable processes in a different species. The accuracy with which a theory predicts the outcome of experiments, whether specifically designed to test it or not, is an excellent indicator of its validity.

Theories may account for biological phenomena from several different perspectives: historical, causal, mechanistic and functional. Historical explanations account for present situations in terms of more remote or 'ultimate' causes, such as phylogeny, the evolutionary history of the species, or ontogeny, the development and life history of the individual. Explanations may be more 'proximate', either causal, e.g. the birds flew off the bird-table because they saw the cat hiding in the bushes; mechanistic, e.g. wings, light skeletons, large, powerful muscles and an excellent sense of balance enable birds to fly; or functional, e.g. birds avoid being killed because they watch continuously for predators and fly away when necessary. Many of the most useful theories incorporate more than one of these four kinds of explanation, as indicated in Chapter 1.

Theories start as **hypotheses**, propositions that appear to explain certain observations or facts, and require several separate kinds of further evidence, preferably experimental evidence, to become accepted as theories.

3.2.1 THE FORMULATION OF A MAJOR BIOLOGICAL THEORY

These days, nearly everybody knows that chemical processes in living organisms are basically similar to those of the abiotic world of rocks, the atmosphere, etc. But until the 18th century, even highly educated people believed in a 'vital force' which made life fundamentally different from non-living matter. During the period now called the Enlightenment, scientists began to think carefully about the relationship between air, fire and life. The English nonconformist minister and schoolmaster, Joseph Priestley (1733–1804), noted that a candle burned and a mouse lived for longer if they were confined separately in sealed jars than if they were kept together inside a similar vessel. He concluded that living mice and burning candles compete for the same component of air, but he did not name the limiting resource, nor attempt to quantify how the animal and the flame use it. In fact, this conclusion was difficult to integrate with the theory about the mechanism of combustion that he (and almost everyone else) then believed.

Antoine Lavoisier was a brilliant amateur chemist with very wide interests (Figure 3.1). He isolated and named oxygen as the component of air that most readily reacted with a wide range of different substances, and accurately measured the proportions in which it combined with various elements, including tin, lead, silver, mercury and phosphorus as well as carbon, the principal component of living tissues. In 1783, he enlisted the collaboration of Pierre Laplace (Figure 3.2) on a new venture to extend this research into what we would now call biochemistry.

Lavoisier and Laplace sought evidence to support their hypothesis that animals use air in the same way as burning minerals. Together they designed apparatus to measure the 'air used' by a guinea-pig confined in a small container, and the heat its body produced over 75 minutes. These measurements formed the basis of calculations that demonstrated an equivalence between the heat produced and air 'consumed' by burning charcoal and by a living animal.

By making measurements that were sufficiently accurate to show that the processes were quantitatively similar, Lavoisier and Laplace converted Priestley's vaguely formulated idea into a fully fledged theory that proclaimed the fundamental similarity between respiration (of living organisms) and combustion (of non-living minerals). The idea challenged long-standing notions about the mechanism of combustion and the nature of life, and thus it took some time to be universally accepted. All biologists now believe that in spite of the superficial

Figure 3.1   Antoine Lavoisier (1743–1794) was a French civil servant, landowner and amateur scientist. He set up a private laboratory in Paris and funded his important and original research out of his huge personal fortune until he was arrested and guillotined by revolutionaries at the age of 50.

contrasts, and differences in intermediate reactions, the overall chemical transformations of combustion and aerobic respiration are similar.

Two hundred years of research have extended and refined Lavoisier's basic theory of respiration. As well as establishing a new principle that has stood the test of time, the experiments of Lavoisier and Laplace inspired later investigators to study physiology in a quantitative way. The study of isolated tissues and of a much wider range of species has shown that some organisms and tissues sometimes or always respire without using oxygen.

Modern biologists often plan new experiments or set out to collect and examine previously unstudied fossil or living species, with the expressed intention of 'testing' the exact predictions of a particular aspect of a theory. Often, as in this example, the first such investigations are carried out by the proponents of the initial hypothesis, to be followed by further studies on other species, or using more rigorous methods. In other cases, data emerge from an unconnected line of research that appear to be inconsistent with established theoretical concepts. Whatever its source, if the new evidence is not in accordance with the theory, scientists are faced with a dilemma. *Either* the data are dismissed as unsound because the experiments are badly designed, the observations not what they purport to be, or the measurements technically flawed, *or* the theory has to be revised to accommodate the new findings.

Even long-established theories are continually challenged and may be drastically revised or even abandoned altogether. As hinted in the previous chapters, biologists are still far from agreeing on a single, universally accepted system for classifying all organisms. New species, even whole new categories of organisms, continue to be discovered, requiring radical revision of hitherto established theories about the number and status of taxonomic categories and their relationship to each other (see Chapter 1).

Theories about basic biological mechanisms are equally susceptible to being overturned, even when they have held sway in an active field of research for many years. Challenges may come from unexpected sources as well as from experiments designed to test a theory's predictions. Sometimes accommodating new information simply requires only minor adjustments to the existing concepts, but in a few cases, routine laboratory measurements seem to contradict the basic tenets of established theories.

3.2.2 PRIONS

During the last 15 years of the 20th century, there was much public concern about the rapid spread of a hitherto unknown disease among domesticated cattle called bovine spongiform encephalopathy, known colloquially as BSE or mad cow disease. Affected animals became poorly coordinated and prone to aggressive behaviour and panic, deteriorating rapidly within weeks of the first symptoms being noticed. No treatment could cure the disease or even delay its progress, and what was even more alarming, it appeared to be transmissible, passing between members of a herd. Post-mortem examination of the brains and spinal cords of cattle in the advanced stages of BSE revealed 'holes' where nerve cells had disintegrated, producing the sponge-like appearance for which the disease is

Figure 3.2 The French scientist, Pierre Laplace (1749–1827) was primarily a mathematician and astronomer but he also collaborated with Lavoisier to design apparatus for chemical and biological research that was far ahead of its time for accuracy and reliability.

named. Both the symptoms and the defects in microscopical appearance of the brain resemble those of a disease of sheep called scrapie, and certain rare human diseases. A particle named a **prion** was isolated from the affected tissues, that seemed to be transmissible: within weeks of being inoculated with it, laboratory mice developed symptoms and alterations of brain structure similar to those of cattle with BSE.

The genetic materials DNA or RNA (usually both) could be found in all infectious particles hitherto identified, including all kinds of viruses, bacteria, fungi, protoctists and parasitic worms. The theory was that infectious agents worked either by making their own proteins and replicating themselves, or by acting as genes or gene regulatory agents, hijacking their host's protein synthesizing machinery to make 'their' protein and more of their DNA or RNA. They must contain at least some DNA or RNA and anything that lacked these essential ingredients could not replicate itself and so infect other animals. The problem was that chemical analysis of prions appeared to show that they consist only of protein. Even the most sensitive methods applied to the purest, most concentrated material failed to demonstrate the presence of either DNA or RNA in the prions.

Which is wrong, the theory of what constitutes an infectious agent, or the biochemical techniques used to detect the all-important DNA and RNA? The argument over prions raged for a decade. At first, the theory dominated the observations, and reports of prions consisting only of proteins were dismissed as technically flawed. Such criticism is difficult to refute entirely: no biochemical assay is 100% reliable on all kinds of organisms. However, this position became harder to justify as more and more data suggested that, notwithstanding their eccentricities, all-protein prions really did pervert mammalian brain cells into making abnormal proteins.

Protein chemists and biochemists eventually took such data seriously enough to think about how such a process might occur, and suggested some hypotheses. However, they have not turned out to be easy to test experimentally, and at the time of writing, laboratory investigators are far from agreed about whether any of the proposed mechanisms actually operate. Although the prion theory's chief proponent, the American biochemist, Dr Stanley Prusiner, was awarded the Nobel Prize in Physiology or Medicine in 1997, not everyone is yet convinced: some respected biologists still believe that prions have some nucleic acids lurking in them, which established techniques have failed to extract.

A routine investigation into the cause of BSE did lead to revision of one of the most firmly established theories in biochemistry. Concepts about what constitutes a pathogen had to be changed to accommodate the notion that proteins could influence the conformation, and hence the biological activity, of other proteins without involving nucleic acids. In the case of prions, the laboratory evidence is ahead of theory: we have observations that cannot easily be incorporated into the existing theoretical framework. Sometimes the converse happens, and hypotheses, such as that discussed in Box 3.1, wait a long time for the development of techniques capable of providing data that support or refute them convincingly.

Box 3.1 MOLECULAR BIOLOGY SUPPORTS A 200-YEAR-OLD HYPOTHESIS

Étienne Geoffroy Saint-Hilaire (Figure 3.3) was director of the world's first municipal zoo in Paris for 47 years, greatly enlarging the collections and promoting the popularity of zoology among ordinary people as well as scientists. As a young man, he served as a scientific expert on Napoleon's Egyptian campaign and was stranded in Egypt for three years with the surviving troops, whose evacuation was prevented by a blockade of British warships. He occupied the time with thoughtful observations and thorough dissections of a wide variety of animals. In 1822, he proposed that arthropods and vertebrates shared a common ancestor: the position of the nerve cord, gut, etc. had simply been inverted in one lineage relative to the other, as indicated in Figure 3.4.

Further research in comparative anatomy, embryology and palaeontology provided little support for this hypothesis, and some observations appeared to rule it out. In spite of the efforts of several powerful advocates, the idea was not generally accepted until the mid 1990s, when DNA sequencing and detailed studies of the molecular mechanisms of early development in fruit-flies (arthropods) and toads (vertebrates) produced new kinds of comparative data. Molecular biologists showed that the genes that induce the arthropod ventral nerve cord are so similar to those that form the (dorsal) spinal cord of vertebrates, that the fly gene can work in toads. Such similarity could only have arisen from common ancestry, suggesting that the French zoologist's hypothesis could be right after all.

Figure 3.3 Étienne Geoffroy Saint-Hilaire (1772–1844).

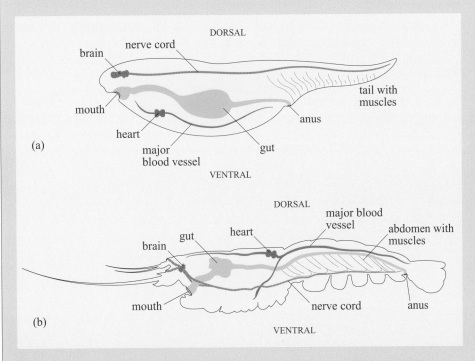

Figure 3.4 Basic body plan of (a) a vertebrate and (b) an arthropod, showing the positions of the nerve cord, gut and major blood vessels.

As more rival hypotheses compete to be accepted as theories, so more accurate observations and better designed, more carefully executed experiments are required to choose between them. Obtaining relevant data depends upon suitable instrumentation and specimens for study. Technical advances have greatly extended the range of features that can be measured, so nearly all kinds of practical research have become quicker and more accurate.

Biological theories have also benefited enormously from progress in non-laboratory sciences, especially pure mathematics and computing. Many theories now take the form of **mathematical models** which integrate new hypotheses with data from experiments or observations. The use of computers allows large amounts of information to be analysed and exact, quantifiable predictions made which can be tested by further measurements. Other theories involve vaguer notions such as that of a '**trade-off**' between competing physiological functions, such as bodily growth and reproduction. It is important to realize that comparing the trade-offs between life processes does not imply any similarity of physiological mechanism, and thus cannot explain the observations mechanistically.

SUMMARY OF SECTION 3.2

1   Hypotheses become established as theories when sufficient evidence supports them, and are continually revised and re-evaluated. Support for new hypotheses is often delayed until technical advances enable relevant evidence to be obtained.

2   Even long-established theories can be overturned by new information which may come from investigations that appear to be irrelevant to their main tenets.

3.3   OBSERVATIONS

Observation of the structure, habits and geographical distribution of living and fossil organisms is the longest established kind of biological evidence. Until the late 18th century, collecting and cataloguing preserved plants and animals, and watching living specimens were almost the only sources of biological information, but nonetheless supported major theoretical advances in taxonomy, the mechanism of evolution and aspects of nutrition and physiology. Even very simple hypotheses help biologists to organize their observations, and suggest new lines of investigation and kinds of measurements that test predictions.

The theory of evolution by natural selection was based almost entirely on observations: Darwin conducted very few experiments to test its predictions, but he collected and studied a great many specimens from a variety of sources, including South America and the Galapagos Islands, and listened carefully to accounts of other people's observations. He assessed thoroughly how far each observation was consistent with his hypothesis, and if any appeared to be incompatible, he tried to find reasons for the discrepancy. Darwin's approach convinced many people that his theory was true, and scientists did not attempt to study natural selection experimentally until well into the 20th century. The analysis of observations, especially but not exclusively quantitative measurements, is still very useful for interpreting many aspects of animal behaviour, including foraging, sexual and social interactions and breeding strategy.

Experimentation is now pre-eminent in subjects such as biochemistry and physiology, but observation and description are still important for many topics in basic science, especially taxonomy, palaeontology, comparative and functional anatomy, and animal behaviour. They are also important in nearly all aspects of biology applied to humans, pets and zoo animals and rare or endangered species, on whom it is impractical or ethically unacceptable to perform more than the very simplest experiment. Pathology, for example, involves recording detailed observations on tissues collected by biopsy or post-mortem, and comparing the structural and biochemical features of the tissues with the patients' abnormalities in physiology or behaviour. Hypotheses about the causes and course of disorders are constructed, and further observations carefully assessed for being consistent or inconsistent with the initial proposition.

Although human assessment of qualitative features is still important, modern instrumentation has enormously extended the range of features that can be measured, as well as improved the accuracy of measurement. These days, sophisticated biochemical techniques, including DNA sequencing, separation and characterization of proteins and other large molecules, many different kinds of microscopy, and satellite tracking and remotely controlled cameras, permit description and measurement of a huge range of topics in biology, from gene structure to seasonal migration. The enormous quantity of information so obtained is then stored and analysed in powerful computers.

Comparisons of observations of similar structures, processes or activities in many different species have always had an essential part to play both in understanding the relationships between species and in distinguishing fundamental mechanisms from special adaptive features of individual species. The investigation of topics such as the size and internal organization of genes or the course of maturation from zygote to adult may involve making comparable observations on a wide range of species. Some of the most important recent advances in our understanding of the diversity of organisms and the course and mechanism of evolution come from comparing observations on biological molecules and cellular structures and processes.

3.4 EXPERIMENTS

The essence of experiments is intervention and manipulation: the experimenter alters some feature of the organism's environment, genetic inheritance, or physiological capacities, and measures the changes in its behaviour or physiology. The contrasts between the undisturbed or **control** situation and the experimental intervention are then matched to those predicted from the hypothesis.

○ On this definition, which of the investigations described in Section 3.2 were experimental?

● Priestley's studies constitute an experiment to determine the effect of the presence of a burning candle on mouse longevity. Lavoisier and Laplace's investigation was not an experiment. It consisted of detailed, quantitative observations using the most sophisticated apparatus of its time, followed by comparison between the living and the non-living systems.

Experimentation depends upon making suitable equipment, and upon developing ways of intervening in living systems or their environment without disrupting them so much that the organism's physiology is grossly distorted in so many ways that it becomes impossible to determine what has caused what. Ideally, the intervention is slight and reversible, so the control measurements can be conducted on the same organisms after the experimental procedure as well as before it. One way of achieving this ideal is to manipulate the organism or cell only in ways that it would normally encounter in its natural habitat. But that, of course, entails knowing about what situations the organism normally tolerates.

Where the intervention is irreversible, or the organisms have to be killed to obtain tissues for analysis, the experimental subjects are divided into groups that are as similar as possible in features such as age, sex, genetic inheritance, dietary history, etc. The experimental procedure is applied to one group, while the other serves as the controls, experiencing the same conditions except for the feature under investigation.

3.4.1 EXPERIMENTAL STUDY OF SYMBIOSIS

The previous chapter described several instances of contrasting kinds of organisms living in intimate, permanent association. These assemblages seemed to be specific and functional, but in most cases, there was no experimental evidence that supports or refutes the hypothesis that they actually were so.

Hydras (Figure 3.5) are invertebrate animals (phylum Cnidaria) that have long been used in laboratory teaching and research, because of their sessile habits and simple structure and because, unlike almost all other cnidarians, they live in freshwater.

Like most cnidarians, hydras are predators on other animals: the long tentacles on each 'bud' (called a hydranth) catch prey and pass it into the sac-like body (called the enteron), where it is digested and the nutrients absorbed. *Hydra viridis* is green because the cells lining the enteron contain unicellular algae. The number of algae is fairly constant at about 12–25 per cell and they pass between generations with the eggs, suggesting that they may be symbionts, exchanging nutrients with the animal cells.

○ What experiments would test the hypothesis that the algae contribute to the nutrition of *H. viridis*?

● Compare the growth (or reproduction, or both) of initially similar hydras with and without their algae, and with and without access to animal food.

The biologists who performed such experiments in the early 1960s measured growth by counting the numbers of hydranths in colonies. The stock were

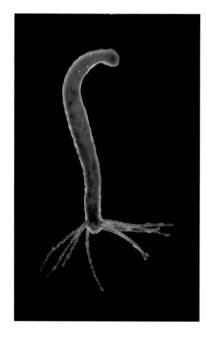

Figure 3.5 Adult *Hydra viridis* live in ponds and shallow, slow-flowing streams attached to stones or vegetation. They catch prey on their long, trailing tentacles.

maintained in clean water containing only mineral salts, exposed to natural daylight and fed daily on tiny shrimp larvae, one of many kinds of prey that they eat in the wild. Methods were then devised for artificially removing the algae to create living, growing, alga-free hydras, and for re-introducing them when required. The experimenters counted the hydranths in colonies of green and alga-free hydras kept under different feeding regimes. Their data are shown in Figure 3.6. To fit the wide range of values onto the graph, the vertical scale is logarithmic, which also makes the lines appear straighter than on a linear scale.

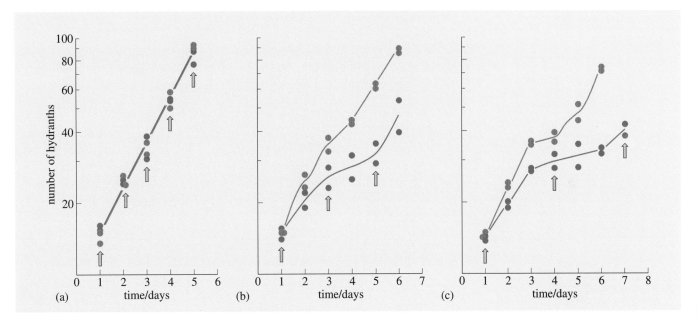

Figure 3.6 Growth of green (green symbols) and alga-free (brown symbols) *H. viridis* kept in the light with different feeding regimes: (a) fed daily with brine shrimp larvae; (b) fed every second day; (c) fed every third day. The yellow arrows indicate feeding days. Data from Muscatine and Lenhoff (1965).

○ What does the experiment summarized in Figure 3.6 show?

● When the hydras were given animal food every day, there was no difference in the growth of green and alga-free specimens, but when they were fed less often, the presence of symbiotic algae increased the number of new hydranths produced.

More detailed studies showed that in the absence of any prey, bud formation over a period of 12 days is proportional to the number of symbiotic algae in the hydras. The experimenters concluded that when animal food is plentiful, the algae are not essential to the growth of *H. viridis* but when prey are scarce, they supplement its energy supply with their photosynthetic products.

These experiments do not prove conclusively that this theory is correct. Almost all data can be interpreted on an alternative hypothesis. For example, those in Figure 3.6 could be showing that the algae help in catching or digesting the prey but contribute no nutrients themselves.

○ How could you test this alternative hypothesis? What further experiments or observations would support the original hypothesis?

● This hypothesis could be tested by observing the fate of the prey fed to the hydras. If the food appears in the enteron, is broken down and its nutrients taken into the cells at equal rates in both green and colourless hydras, the hypothesis is refuted. The original hypothesis would be strengthened by demonstrating that these results depend upon prolonged, regular exposure to daylight and/or that sugars formed by photosynthesis in the algae are used by or incorporated into the tissues of the hydras.

Further alternative hypotheses are limited only by the investigators' imagination and critical abilities, and the only constraints on the testing of these hypotheses are the investigators' experimental ingenuity and the instrumentation available to them.

○ How would reliance upon symbiotic algae affect where and when *H. viridis* could live?

● The algae can only contribute to the hydra's nutrition when regularly exposed to enough daylight to support photosynthesis, which would restrict the animal to unshaded surface waters. It could only grow rapidly during the long, bright days of summer.

Those hydras that rely on animal food could live in deep water or shady pools, and indeed anywhere that suitable prey were abundant. The 'option' of living with or without symbionts extends the animal's range and abundance.

○ Referring to Section 3.2, what kind of hypothesis is tested by the experiments in Figure 3.6? What kind of experiments would be necessary to support another kind of explanation for the presence of algae in hydras?

● The experiments support a *functional* hypothesis for the presence of symbiotic algae. A *mechanistic* explanation for the association requires investigations into how the symbiosis forms and/or how nutrients pass from algae to animal.

To investigate the mechanisms involved in algae becoming symbionts, alga-free hydras were experimentally induced to take up the symbiotic species of algae, or similar algae that do not usually form a symbiosis, or dead algae, or inorganic particles of similar size. A few days later, the fates of these items in macerated hydra cells were observed with the light or electron microscope. The symbiotic algae entered the cells at the surface exposed to the enteron and migrated, enclosed in a membrane, to the opposite side of the cells where they divided until a fixed number were formed. All the other kinds of particles tested were collected together in a large vesicle and expelled out of the cells.

○ What does this experiment show about the *mechanism* of symbiosis?

● It reveals that hydra cells can recognize their own symbiotic algae, and actively move them to where they would be exposed to light. All other foreign material is ejected.

Such specificity suggests that *Hydra viridis* and its algae have evolved adaptations to living as symbionts. Further studies revealed mechanisms that enable sugars synthesized by the algae to pass into the animal cells.

3.4.2 VARIABLE DATA

Biological data are rarely as tidy as those obtained from measurements in physics or chemistry. Data obtained from biological experiments and observations are inherently inexact: it may be impossible to get close enough to measure the feature accurately, or the property may change irregularly with time, making precision irrelevant as well as impractical. Most biochemical and physiological measurements involve handling low concentrations of fragile molecules that may deteriorate while the assay is in progress. Even genetically identical organisms raised under similar conditions do not necessarily respond in exactly the same way to an experimental situation.

The problem can be reduced by repeating the experimental procedures on the same organisms, or performing replicate experiments on several specimens and/or measuring several similar samples. The arithmetic average, or **mean** of all the data is then calculated. A statistical measure called **variance** expresses the range of deviation of the data from their mean. Further statistical tests are then applied to the mean and to the variance of the data from the control and experimental systems, to calculate the probability that the two means are really different. Repeated experiments allow the resolution of smaller differences between two means; but statistics reveal only a probability — we can rarely be absolutely sure.

○ Is there any indication from Figure 3.6 that the investigators tried to improve the precision of their experiment using such methods?

● Yes. There are two data points for each day for both green and alga-free colonies of *H. viridis*, indicating that the experiment was duplicated. Lines representing the means of the two sets of data are drawn between the points showing replicate measurements.

Duplication of the experiment revealed substantial variation between apparently similar organisms. The design and data analysis of this experiment, which was performed in the 1960s, would not be acceptable for an academic journal today: there are insufficient replicates and the lines between the means have been drawn by eye. The use of calculators and computers now makes it easy to apply rigorous mathematical techniques which fit lines to data exactly and quantify the probability that deductions from variable data are valid.

Statistical reasoning indicates that if the experimental subjects or analytical methods are inherently variable, the 'pay-off' in terms of improved accuracy of making large numbers of measurements (i.e. hundreds instead of tens) becomes very small. For their conclusions to be widely accepted, experiments must be repeatable in other laboratories. If replicate experiments produce discrepant results, a convincing explanation must be offered, e.g. a different species was used, or the laboratory conditions were substantially different. Experiments that prove impossible to replicate are rejected as invalid.

○ In Figure 3.6, were the data from the experimentally manipulated (algae-free) animals more or less variable than those from the controls? Can you explain your answer?

● More variable. Organisms' reactions to unnatural, possibly stressful situations are often variable. Some hydras may have had more nutrient stores than others, enabling them to sustain a higher growth rate even when starved, at least for a few days.

Organisms in the wild differ not only in age, sex, and the experiences they have had, but also in the combinations of genes they have inherited. Populations without these individual differences would be unlikely to last long in evolutionary time, because they lack the variation necessary to produce offspring equipped to tolerate changes in the environment. The best experiments involve comparing organisms in which only one or a few parameters of the organism or its environment are different. So experimentalists want to study organisms that are as similar as possible in all these ways. Inbred laboratory strains are usually preferred for experimental research because they are genetically much more uniform than their wild relatives.

We think of experiments as elucidating internal mechanisms of physiology and biochemistry, and they have been very important for advances in these aspects of biology. Not all experiments take place in the laboratory or involve specialized apparatus. Some of the most informative are technically simple and can be performed in natural environments; for example, removing or introducing a herbivore into a field or a forest, or placing an artificial reef on the sea floor. Conversely, not all analyses conducted in laboratories are experimental in nature: increasingly elaborate techniques are used to measure and catalogue the structure of proteins, the DNA sequence of genes and other molecular 'observations'. In biology, more than in most other sciences, observational and experimental investigations are intimately interconnected.

SUMMARY OF SECTIONS 3.3 AND 3.4

1 Hypotheses can be tested by both observations and experiments, and both kinds of investigation can be performed in the wild, or in the laboratory, or both.

2 Observations on living and dead organisms formed the first source of biological evidence and are still important for many kinds of research. Sophisticated sensors, measuring devices and analytical techniques greatly extend the range and accuracy of observations and allow wild species to be recorded undisturbed.

3 Experiments involve some kind of intervention that ideally affects only one or a few tissues, organs or actions. The data from the experimental material are compared with those from control organisms that are similar in every respect except that they did not experience the intervention.

4 Almost all observations and experiments used to support a hypothesis are open to interpretation on an alternative hypothesis that can only be eliminated (or supported) by further investigations.

5   Data from both observations and experiments can be analysed using statistics and may form the basis of mathematical models.

3.5 LABORATORY ORGANISMS

Some biologists seem to spend an inordinate length of time watching small flies disporting themselves in bottles, or tiny worms crawling around in plastic dishes covered with an extract of seaweed. Unexceptional-looking weeds with small white flowers are grown in huge quantities. These species have little direct impact on our own lives: they do not attack or poison people, and do not carry diseases, and they have no economic use as food or as a producer of useful materials, but their natural structure and habits make them unusually convenient for experimental research. The scientific questions investigated are often not even relevant to developing means of controlling their abundance or activities: the study of mouse genetics and metabolism has done little to improve the efficiency of mouse traps!

Genetics, cell biology and biochemistry are topics in which almost all recent discoveries arise from the study of only a few laboratory species. It was not always so. Early experiments into the mechanism of heredity concerned topics as diverse as the texture and colour of seeds and plant size in garden peas, shape and texture of the 'comb' on the heads of domestic poultry and coat colour in rabbits, mice, squirrels, guinea-pigs and other small mammals. Fundamental discoveries of lasting importance were made using these species, but these days, the great majority of investigations into gene inheritance and gene action (and most other topics in basic biochemistry and physiology) involve one or other of fewer than a dozen organisms that have come to be known as laboratory species.

○   How could the variability of experimental biological data be minimized?

●   One way is to start with organisms that are as similar as possible in ancestry, age and developmental history.

Such uniformity is much more easily achieved with organisms that can be bred and raised in captivity as required. Factors such as short life cycle and ease of breeding in captivity have facilitated the adoption of certain species for this role, but their most important advantages arise from their suitability for modern analytical methods. Identification and exploitation of these peculiarities often involve careful observation of their internal structure and natural habits. While one important criterion for breeding an organism for research purposes is its amenability to experimental intervention, as pointed out in the previous section, observations are also important to the development and testing of hypotheses, so the term 'laboratory species' is preferable to 'experimental species'. The theories and investigative techniques developed from the study of laboratory organisms often prove to be applicable to species that do impinge directly on our lives, as domestic animals, crop plants and their pollinators or pathogens.

3.5.1 *DROSOPHILA*

Figure 3.7 Adult *Drosophila*, including a wild-type specimen with red eyes (upper left) and a mutant with white eyes (lower left). This mutation was among the first to be identified in laboratory colonies, and has been extensively studied over many years.

After rats and mice, the fruit-fly, *Drosophila*, has the longest and most distinguished career as a laboratory animal (Figure 3.7). A common species, *D. melanogaster*, often seen in homes and gardens in the summer, has been bred in captivity for scientific research for a century. Several zoologists started breeding fruit-flies in the early 1900s, among them Dr Nettie Stevens, a researcher and teacher at Bryn Mawr, one of the leading women's colleges in America. She studied the microscopic structure of chromosomes during the formation of eggs and sperm in a wide variety of insects, including aphids, beetles, cockroaches, crickets, termites and moths, and was among the first biologists to identify the X and Y chromosomes as a fundamental mechanism of sex determination. She noted in passing that all species of *Drosophila* had a haploid chromosome number of only four, which is fewer than most insects and most other animals and plants.

Her colleague Dr Thomas Morgan realized that this feature of *Drosophila*, combined with its short life cycle and convenience of breeding in captivity, offered enormous advantages for research into genetics. After he moved to Columbia University in New York City in 1904, Morgan started breeding fruit-flies on a large scale, and over the next 30 years he and others made many important discoveries about gene linkage and recombination, the mechanisms of meiosis and gene mutation.

Drosophila is a two-winged fly (phylum Arthropoda, class Insecta, order Diptera), related to blowflies, houseflies, mosquitoes, etc. Flies, like many other insects such as beetles, butterflies and bees, have 'indirect development': the eggs hatch into larvae, which feed voraciously and grow rapidly, moulting their cuticle three times (forming stages called instars) until they form a resting stage called a pupa, from which emerges the adult imago which has wings and mature sex organs. The grub-like larvae can be cultured in small tubes or dishes, and the adult flies can be quickly and reversibly immobilized with carbon dioxide or ether for examination under a microscope. Most wild *Drosophila* eat soft, ripe fruit, but in captivity, they are easily raised on an artificial diet made from yeast and molasses.

Under optimum conditions, development from egg to adult is completed in 14 days, and the adults, which weigh about 2 mg, live for about a month. Fertilization is internal and mating is preceded by quite elaborate courtship behaviour, involving visual and auditory signals that people as well as potential mates can easily observe, and so can study.

The cuticle, which covers the entire body, has an elaborate structure that reflects the segmental organization of the underlying soft tissues. The formation of the body segments, and many superficial features such as 'bristles' (hair-like sensory projections of the cuticle), the articulated joints on the limbs and antennae, and the facets of the eye, lend themselves to quantification so are particularly suitable for the study of inheritance and development. Like many invertebrates, *Drosophila* is robust and individuals with abnormalities such as duplicated or deleted body segments, deformed limbs or discoloured eyes develop to adulthood, though they may be unable to breed. These features have provided biologists with an excellent opportunity for studying the mechanisms of gene inheritance and action.

POLYTENE CHROMOSOMES

Thirty years after Morgan established *Drosophila* as the major organism for genetic research, another peculiar feature of fly chromosomes began to be exploited. The unusually large **polytene chromosomes** (Figure 3.8) have been used as a major tool in the study of chromosome structure and its heritable alterations, and the mechanism of gene activation, almost continuously since the early 1930s. Polytene chromosomes are present in various tissues for much of the fly's life, but the most abundant and most readily manipulated material is found in the salivary glands of large third-instar larvae, just before they pupate and develop into adult flies.

The larvae feed by 'spitting out' a solution of enzymes that breaks up yeast and soft plant tissues, and sucking in the resulting liquid, much as blowfly 'maggots' do when feeding on decaying flesh. The salivary glands which produce these secretions are proportionately very large, occupying much of the head, and grow mainly by cell enlargement, not cell proliferation.

○ In such cells, which would be more important, chromosome duplication or gene transcription to form messenger RNA?

● Gene transcription, because the cells are synthesizing large quantities of protein for secretion.

Perhaps to hasten production of messenger RNA, the salivary gland cells make up to 1000 copies of their nuclear DNA which, for reasons that are not entirely clear, remain together as multistrand or 'polytene' chromosomes instead of forming a diffuse mass as happens in most kinds of non-dividing cells. The exceptionally large, banded chromosomes so formed (Figure 3.8) are about 100 times thicker than those of dividing cells and were first described more than 120 years ago (see Box 3.2).

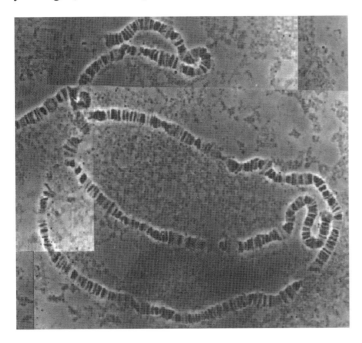

Figure 3.8 Polytene chromosomes in the nucleus of a salivary gland cell of a larval *Drosophila*. This composite image is taken through a powerful microscope (hence the messy background).

20 µm

Contrary to what was first thought, the bands do not correspond exactly to single genes, but they are distinctive and consistent enough to allow visible changes in chromosome structure to be correlated with heritable alterations in gene linkage. Some bands puff up while they are transcribed, enabling the messenger RNA and proteins involved in gene regulation to be collected with tiny pipettes. This material provided the first means of studying gene transcription in higher animals.

BOX 3.2   THE DISCOVERY OF POLYTENE CHROMOSOMES

Naturalists studying cells under powerful microscopes noticed the peculiar appearance of the chromosomes of certain wild flies, and reported their observations as a curiosity 50 years before laboratory-based scientists thought of exploiting polytene chromosomes for studying gene action. The first report of banded chromosomes in the salivary glands of the larvae of non-biting midges (*Chironomus*) appeared in 1881, and between the 1880s and 1920s, several investigators observed large chromosomes in certain somatic cells of various arthropods.

The polytene chromosomes of the aquatic larvae of blackflies (*Simulium* spp.) and biting midges (*Culicoides* spp.), dipteran flies that breed prolifically in unpolluted ponds and streams throughout northern Europe and America, are even easier to stain, and provide clearer images under the microscope than those of *Drosophila*. But by the time biologists turned their attention to the structure and mode of action of genes in somatic cells, breeding experiments had already yielded a great deal of information about the inheritance of fruit-fly genes. *Drosophila* are easier to breed in large numbers in a small space on an artificial diet, and when they escape, as laboratory animals invariably do, they do not suck the scientists' blood, a very irritating habit of female blackflies, mosquitoes and midges. However, the polytene chromosomes of other dipteran flies are still studied for certain kinds of investigation.

We still cannot explain exactly why the salivary glands of fly larvae have these curious properties: many other secretory tissues work perfectly well without polytene chromosomes. The question: 'What is the natural function?' is more often posed by ecologists and behaviourists than by geneticists and cell biologists. They are more likely to ask: 'How does it work?', 'How can we manipulate its activities?' However, functional explanations often emerge from physiological studies. Perhaps future research into polytene chromosomes will provide an answer.

By the 1970s, research into mutation and gene inheritance was almost exhausted, but *Drosophila*'s role as a laboratory organism took on a new lease of life after 1983 when it was discovered that the genes that control early embryonic development and the organization of the basic body plan in this species also function in vertebrates (and in almost all other animals). Now known as Hox genes, they prove to be fundamental to generating basic animal body form (see Box 3.1); their equivalents have not been found in plants, fungi or other eukaryotes. Studying the internal structure of these important genes, and how they act during development of *Drosophila* are just as informative and a lot more convenient than using mice, fish or frogs for similar research.

WILD *DROSOPHILA*

As well as its role as a laboratory organism, the genus *Drosophila* has also been extensively studied in the wild since the 1950s. A great deal is now known about the 2000 or more species (of which 31 occur naturally in Britain) which differ, sometimes only very slightly, in structure, diet and aspects of their behaviour, especially that associated with courtship. Species native to Hawaii and other isolated islands have evolved some particularly unusual and striking structures, behaviours and dietary habits. Their comparative study has led to important advances in our understanding of how species form and how behaviour evolves. Hypotheses developed from research in these natural 'laboratories' of evolution can be combined with those from comparatively short-term study of flies bred and raised under controlled, artificial conditions, to produce integrated theories of the mechanism of evolution.

The importance of having the opportunity, and the inclination, to study the genetics, physiology and habits of organisms in the wild as well as in the laboratory cannot be underestimated: it helps us to distinguish between natural and artificially induced processes, and shows us which of the many phenomena that we observe in the laboratory actually happen in the wild. *Drosophila* has remained in the scientific spotlight for so long because behaviourists, ecologists, physiologists and molecular biologists have joined the geneticists in the study of this diverse genus of hardy flies.

3.5.2 *CAENORHABDITIS*

Until the mid-1960s, the soil worm *Caenorhabditis elegans* was known to a handful of experts as one of hundreds of species of threadworms (phylum Nematoda) that live in the soil. By the end of the 20th century, many millions of these harmless, inconspicuous, economically unimportant little worms had been bred in the laboratory, and studied by hundreds of dedicated biologists, using the most sophisticated techniques available. As a result of their efforts, the genetics, molecular biology, development and behaviour of *C. elegans* are more thoroughly understood than those of any other multicellular organism, including ourselves. These discoveries have led to detailed theories about gene action, the control of cell maturation and programmed cell death, the formation of neural connections and many other topics that are relevant to basic science and medicine.

The molecular biologist Dr Sydney Brenner (who had previously made important contributions to the elucidation of the genetic code) first emphasized the advantages of *C. elegans* as a laboratory animal. Mature worms are about 1 mm long and under optimum conditions, they take only three to four days to grow from zygote to adult. They tolerate living at very high densities, and up to 10 000 can be kept on a single Petri dish, about the size of a small saucer, or up to 10^7 in a litre of culture fluid. Most adults are hermaphrodite (i.e. a single individual produces both eggs and sperm) and do not fertilize each other. They can have 350 offspring at a time, and the short life cycle means that up to 10 000 worms a week can be bred from a single hermaphrodite parent. A few males are also produced, and can fertilize the hermaphrodites. Such sexual reproduction creates new combinations of genes.

The genome of *C. elegans* consists of about 19 000 genes, distributed between six chromosomes, which is five times larger than that of simple eukaryotes such as yeast, and, perhaps surprisingly in view of insects' complicated life cycle and intricate adult structure (Figure 3.7), about 50% larger than that of *Drosophila*. However, the nematode genome is only 3% of the size of that of humans (and most other vertebrate animals), and the genes themselves are also simpler than those of higher animals, thus being more amenable to experimental manipulation. With such an array of technical advantages, the complete DNA sequence of *C. elegans* had been determined by 1998.

Sunlight can harm cells, especially while they are dividing, so the outer layers of most organisms contain light-absorbing pigments that protect the internal organs. *C. elegans*, though, normally lives in total darkness in the soil, and the worms are transparent from egg to adulthood. With a special microscope set-up known as Nomarksi optics, individual cells can be clearly seen, even in living specimens, and followed as the animal matures.

Such observations are facilitated by the fact that in nematodes, cell division ends completely in somatic cells (i.e. other than in the gonads) shortly after hatching, so that each fully-formed individual of any one species consists of the same number of cells. Embryologists first reported this unusual property as long ago as 1907, and between 1910 and 1943, it was studied in several different genera of nematodes, including the huge intestinal parasites of horses, but not in *Caenorhabditis* itself. Until the end of the 1960s, constancy of cell number was taught to students as one of the few remarkable features of an otherwise rather dull, anatomically uniform phylum, of which many species are parasites of arthropods and vertebrates (including humans), or invade roots and other plant tissues.

○ Why would the parasitic species be acceptable for research using microscopy but a non-parasitic species be preferred for genetics and cell biology?

● Most parasites cannot complete their life cycle outside of their host so are difficult to breed in captivity. Also, working with living parasites always carries the risk of accidental infection, even if humans are not the usual host. Infection is less of a hazard for microscopists because the tissues are fixed (i.e. killed and preserved).

So *Caenorhabditis* is preferred for modern research, in spite of being smaller than many parasitic nematodes. *C. elegans* worms consist of about 600 cells at hatching, rising to 959 cells (not counting the eggs and sperm) in hermaphrodite adults, while adult males have 1031 cells (compared to around a million in *Drosophila*). We still do not know why they have these fixed numbers of cells, but embryologists have exploited this odd property so efficiently that much is now known about how *C. elegans* develops (Horvitz and Sulston, 1990).

Detailed observations and experiments involving selective destruction of certain cells and single gene mutations have charted the anatomy, development and major functions of each cell. The small size and tough outer cuticle of *Caenorhabditis* make it difficult to manipulate with conventional surgical instruments. However, scientists have developed a quick, efficient means of selectively eliminating one or a small group of cells by shining a tightly focused cone of laser light through the worm's transparent cuticle. When concentrated at the apex of the cone, the focused laser light generates enough heat to kill a single cell after only 1–2 min, while others in the beam's path that are exposed to more diffuse light remain unharmed.

The natural diet of *C. elegans* has been little studied, but in captivity they can be bred on plates lined with agar, on a synthetic diet based on common laboratory bacteria, so it is assumed that they eat soil bacteria in the wild, sucking in their food in a semi-liquid state. Threadworms wriggle with a distinctive thrashing motion, and respond to touch and various other stimuli, actions that presumably form part of their means of escaping from the larger soil animals that prey upon them. The behaviour of *Caenorhabditis* is controlled by just 302 neurons (compared to many millions in arthropods such as lobsters, and billions in vertebrates such as rats), and is highly stereotyped. Unusual behaviour arising from rare gene mutations that alter the maturation of nerves and muscles or neural connections is easily detected just by scanning a dish of worms under a microscope. As a result of studies linking neural structure with behaviour, *C. elegans* is the only animal in which the complete wiring diagram of the nervous system is known.

3.5.3   RATS AND MICE

Small rodents have long been used for scientific research (e.g. Section 3.2.1). Since the beginning of the 20th century, rats, mice and a few other kinds of rodents, including guinea-pigs and hamsters, have been specially bred for scientific and medical research and are by far the most thoroughly studied small mammals. Various features of these species' habits and diet make them particularly suitable as laboratory animals.

The Rodentia are by far the largest order of mammals, numbering at least 1700 species, including squirrels, voles, lemmings, many different kinds of mouse-like creatures, and coypus, capybaras and guinea-pigs. Most wild rodents gnaw on seeds and other dried plant food, but many also eat carrion and large invertebrates, particularly while breeding.

Many species of the family Muridae (rats, mice, hamsters and gerbils) readily colonize new environments and exploit new sources of food. When food is plentiful, they breed prolifically with several generations per year, and reach maturity at an early age. They sometimes become very abundant, and can tolerate living at quite high densities and in novel surroundings. Most murid rodents accept a synthetic diet made from dried grains, but also take a variety of other food. Rats in particular can be persuaded to taste almost any kind of food (certainly almost anything that humans would eat) and can be raised successfully on a wide range of synthetic diets. These convenient habits, and the fact that rats are mammals, make them specially suitable for investigations into aspects of nutrition and toxicology applicable to humans.

House mice (*Mus musculus*) and one species of rat (*Rattus rattus*) have lived off our food stores and shared our habitations for millennia (at least since the Neolithic), so as well as their own rodent diseases, they have also been exposed to many of the parasites and pathogenic microbes that cause disease in humans. This evolutionary 'experience' and the similarity between their physiology and ours, make them particularly suitable for studying the mechanisms of disease and the body's defences against it.

The ancestors of many strains of modern laboratory mice were collected and bred by mouse fanciers, especially in western Europe and Japan, where the selective breeding of unusual-looking animals, pigeons, goldfish, dogs, cats and poultry as well as house mice, was a popular hobby for many years. The 1 000 or so natural mutant strains of mice include those with black, white, ginger and mottled coats, long hair, short hair and even no hair, and strains that readily develop metabolic disorders, ranging from obesity and diabetes to muscular dystrophy and cancer.

Compared to many other species, it is fairly easy to produce pure-bred homozygous mice and rats, because they accept brother–sister matings if no alternative is made available. Both deliberate and unintentional selective breeding have already produced noticeable evolution from the wild ancestors. As well as a wider range of colours, laboratory strains grow faster, mature younger, have larger litters, cannot run as fast and are more docile than their wild relations. Some of the hardiest and most prolific strains of rats and mice are albino, with a white coat and pink eyes (all wild rats and mice are brown or black), though the colour *per se* is irrelevant to their roles as a laboratory animal (Figure 3.9).

Figure 3.9 These albino rats are one of scores of strains of *Rattus* that are bred for research purposes.

The importance of mice in research increased greatly during the 1990s with the development of techniques for the selective deletion of particular genes. Instead of waiting for a random mutation to happen spontaneously, scientists could alter or delete a gene that codes for a molecule of interest. Such '**knock-out**' mice can be used to study the function of gene products, and when and where in the body particular genes become important. Genes can be selectively 'knocked out' in other eukaryotes, including yeast and certain amphibians, but so far, the mouse is the only mammal in which the method works reliably, although in principle, it could be extended to rats and domestic livestock.

Thousands of mice with one or more genes 'knocked out' have been produced for research into basic physiology, developmental biology, and the mechanisms of disease. As so often in biology, the presence of 'back-up' genes and alternative biochemical mechanisms makes the results of many such experiments more difficult to interpret than molecular biologists had hoped. For decades, embryological research concentrated on frogs, the domestic chicken and sea-urchins, but the research that made 'test-tube babies' possible and the spectacular recent advances in knock-out gene techniques mean that more is now known about the embryonic and fetal development of mice than of any other animal.

3.5.4 ARABIDOPSIS

Arabidopsis thaliana (Figure 3.10) is sometimes known as thale cress and belongs to the family Brassicaceae (cabbages, mustard, etc.). The characteristics that make it a successful weed also make it suitable as a laboratory species: a short life cycle (as brief as 6 weeks in optimum conditions) and prolific production of very small (only 20 µg) seeds that can be easily harvested by hand. The small flowers (1–2 mm across) are self-fertile, but can be cross-pollinated if the flower's own anthers are removed. The plant grows up to 30 cm tall and in dense clumps, but the roots are shallow so it can be raised in trays.

The importance of *Arabidopsis* as a laboratory species has increased enormously since the 1980s, when it was discovered to have an exceptionally small nuclear genome, and it is now the most widely studied species for plant genetics and molecular biology. It has 20 000–25 000 genes, distributed over five chromosomes, the smallest known genome for a flowering plant. Although between five and seven times larger than that of common yeasts and 20–50 times larger than that of most bacteria studied, this value is 30 times smaller than the human genome, about the same size as that of *Caenorhabditis* and two-thirds the size of that of *Drosophila*.

Most plants, including garden peas, have larger haploid genomes than humans and some species of the lily family have 10 times as much DNA. After its initial lead as the species in which Mendel discovered random assortment of inherited characters, peas have proved so intractable for further research into the fundamental mechanisms of genetics that they have hardly been used since. Peas and many other crop plants continue to be used for physiological research, and by those seeking to make genetic improvement in crops, but they have been superseded by other species whose special features make them more suitable to the techniques used for modern genetics.

3.4.5 ESCHERICHIA COLI

Escherichia coli (Figure 3.11) has the characteristics of 'good' laboratory organisms: a short life cycle and easy to maintain. This average-sized bacterium (about 2 µm long) occurs naturally in the colon of many vertebrates, including ourselves, but it can be cultured on simple synthetic media up to high population

Figure 3.10 *Arabidopsis thaliana*, a common weed in gardens.

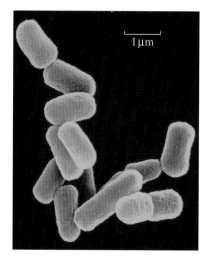

1 μm

Figure 3.11 *Escherichia coli*, a rod-shaped bacterium commonly found in the gut. False colour has been added to the electron micrograph image to enhance the visibility of the bacterial cells. *Escherichia* is named after the German physician, Theodor Escherich (1857–1911), who founded a children's hospital in Vienna and wrote a book about microbes in the human intestine. *E. coli* was not adopted as a laboratory organism until more than 40 years after taxonomists named it, so the doctor probably never anticipated how important his namesake would become.

densities, at least 10^8 cells cm^{-3}. *E. coli* is also hardy and tolerates a range of temperatures. At its optimum of 37 °C, and if supplied with unlimited nutrients, it can divide as often as every 20 minutes, so several generations can be studied in an afternoon.

○ How many *E. coli* would form from $10\,cm^3$ of culture medium containing 50 000 cells per ml after four hours of growth in optimum conditions?

● 2.048×10^9 cells. *E. coli* can divide every 20 min, or 12 times in 4 h ($= 240\,min$), enabling each of the 5×10^4 bacteria to produce $2^{12} = 4096$ progeny. So the final number is $4096 \times (5 \times 10^4) = 2.048 \times 10^8\,cm^{-3}$, or 2.048×10^9 cells in $10\,cm^3$.

With such huge numbers, replicate experiments are less necessary to obtain reliable data, since growth of a single culture involves the maturation and division of millions of cells.

Most eukaryote organisms, including ourselves, are diploid, i.e. have two complete sets of chromosomes. If an allele of a gene is altered in some way, the 'normal' copy in the other set of chromosomes usually produces enough of the gene product to mask any deficiencies. However, bacteria are haploid, with only one set of genes, making the consequences of any mutation immediately obvious. Haploidy has made bacteria very useful for studies of genes, especially gene mutation, and much of what we know about gene control has been discovered using *E. coli*.

Because it is so easy to generate mutants that are unable to synthesize fully functional forms of one or more enzymes, bacteria have been used extensively to investigate biochemical pathways. During the 1950s and 1960s, the genetic code and the mechanisms of gene transcription and protein synthesis were discovered in *E. coli* and some of its natural viruses. More recently, these hardy and versatile laboratory organisms were used to study the role of membranes in ATP synthesis and to develop the basic techniques now used in genetic engineering.

3.5.6 OTHER ORGANISMS IN THE LABORATORY

This account of a few widely used laboratory organisms is by no means exhaustive. Many fundamental discoveries have been made using quite different experimental subjects. Some are chosen for some anatomical or physiological feature that makes them particularly amenable to certain kinds of investigation. If they cannot be bred in the laboratory, the scientists have to move to where they can be found, and work only when they are available. Biologists are still prepared to travel to study rare primitive species, and those belonging to phyla, classes or orders, most of whose members are now extinct, as data from them can help to determine in which common ancestor a feature first appeared. But these days, convenience of maintenance and regular supplies are the primary criteria for the choice of laboratory species.

Experimental physiology began as a branch of medical research so the emphasis was on vertebrates. It proved too difficult to maintain the tissues from mammals and birds at a constant, warm temperature, so those of frogs (*Rana* and related genera) and to a lesser extent, salamanders, were studied. However, although the tadpoles were easy to keep in captivity, it proved extremely difficult to devise a synthetic diet for most adult frogs or toads, except fully aquatic species such as *Xenopus*. Physiologists had to rely upon wild-caught specimens, which became increasingly scarce, and ethical objections to depletion of natural populations were raised. From being the standard experimental vertebrate in the 1930s until the 1960s, the use of frogs in basic physiological research has declined steeply.

For the last 30 years, the zebra-fish, *Danio rerio*, has been widely used for research in embryology, molecular genetics and aspects of toxicology, because its eggs are transparent and take as little as 100 days to grow from hatching to sexual maturity. These hardy, colourful little fish are common in streams and rice paddies of South-East Asia and have long been bred in captivity for display in home aquariums.

By the late 1930s, biologists realized that, in spite of their obvious relevance to humans, vertebrates had serious drawbacks as experimental animals. In vertebrates, spiders and some kinds of worms, the blood is under pressure, and tissues such as muscle, the eye and the kidney do not function normally once they are isolated from the body unless artificially perfused with oxygenated blood. But at least as adults, most arthropods other than spiders do not have high blood pressure, and many of their tissues, including the gut, muscles and the nervous system, readily 'live' outside the body for many hours bathed in a simple salt solution.

Arthropods, and many kinds of soft-bodied animals, also have comparatively few nerve cells, of which many are much larger than vertebrate neurons and are constant in anatomical location. For their size, many invertebrate muscles, especially those of flying insects, are more powerful than those of vertebrates and are controlled by much simpler neural apparatus. The embryonic development of many invertebrates is also much more robust than that of vertebrates, greatly facilitating studies involving altering or deleting genes involved in the formation of particular tissues. And, of course, using simpler animals that could be bred in captivity was cheaper and avoided many of the ethical issues raised by using vertebrates. Table 3.1 summarizes the special features of a few of the many invertebrates that physiologists have used to study particular topics since the 1930s. These organisms, together with the species discussed in this section, produced many spectacular advances in physiology, biochemistry and cell biology.

To be accepted as representing basic mechanisms, a process or structure must be demonstrated in several contrasting species — an insect, a snail and a fish, for example. Often experience with techniques developed on one particularly 'easy' species can be adapted for use on others whose structure is less well suited and

Table 3.1   Some invertebrate animals used for research in basic physiology.

Species	Higher classification	Main advantages in the laboratory	Principal uses
	Arthropoda		
Rhodnius bed-bug	Insecta, Hemiptera	Mostly sedentary, until a single large meal of mammalian blood triggers moulting.	Moulting and growth in insects
Schistocerca migratory locust	Insecta, Orthoptera	Large insect, easily bred in captivity in dense crowds; eats almost any plants (important agricultural pest in Africa); powerful muscles controlled by relatively few neurons; flies well while restrained.	Basic neurobiology, sensory and muscle physiology; control of movement and posture
Manduca tobacco hornworm	Insecta, Lepidoptera	Large, easy to breed, important agricultural pest. Finds food and mates by smell.	Sensory and digestive physiology
Limulus horsehoe-crab	Chelicerata, Merostomata	Very large and docile; eye of typical arthropod structure but with larger, more accessible components.	Physiology of vision
	Mollusca		
Loligo squid	Cephalopoda	Not easy to keep in captivity, but swimming muscles controlled by 'giant' neurons which are large enough and robust enough for detailed experiments on parts of single cells.	Basic mechanism of formation of action potentials in neurons
Octopus common octopus	Cephalopoda	Bottom-dwelling scavenger that lives in shallow water, so easy to keep in captivity; vision and tactile senses well developed; learns readily.	Basic mechanisms of vision and learning
Aplysia, Tritonia sea-slugs	Gastropoda	Simple nervous system contains exceptionally large neurons, many of distinct colour and fixed position. Escapes by swimming with stereotyped movements. Can learn to avoid harm.	Basic neural mechanisms of movement control and memory formation
	Annelida		
Hirudo medicinalis medicinal leech	Hirudinia	Can be bred in captivity; simple nervous system contains large neurons arranged in a chain of similar ganglia. Neural connections are controlled by a relatively few genes.	Growth and development of neural connections
	Echinodermata		
Echinus sea-urchin	Echinoidea	Production of eggs and sperm can be controlled; eggs transparent and convenient in size; embryonic development robust.	Fertilization; early embryonic development

would have proved very tricky if they had been studied initially. There is always a chance that a property at first thought to be basic and universal turns out, in the light of further investigation, to be a special feature of a particular group of organisms and does not represent the majority.

Many important discoveries owe as much to wisdom and good luck in selecting the right organisms for investigating a particular topic as to using sophisticated apparatus and biochemical assays. The discovery of 'new' experimental organisms often depends upon biochemists and other laboratory-based scientists taking an interest in the observations of field biologists and taxonomists. Equally, field biologists have to be able and willing to use some laboratory techniques, such as a powerful microscope, to have a chance of finding unusual structures in 'exotic' species.

The suitability of all the laboratory organisms described in the previous sections was established from observations of their habits in the wild, and peculiarities of their physiology or microscopic structure.

○ What were the contributions of (a) comparative biology and (b) new laboratory techniques to the establishment of *Drosophila* as an experimental organism (Section 3.5.1)?

● (a) Noting that, compared to other insects, *Drosophila* had unusually few chromosomes, and that they were sometimes exceptionally large (polytene); studying their natural diet and life cycle to develop means of breeding them in captivity. (b) Recording and breeding natural mutants; inducing mutations artificially; investigating linkage between genes; visualizing and controlling puffs on polytene chromosomes, and many more.

As pointed out in Section 3.5.2, one of the main advantages of *Caenorhabditis* for research into molecular and cell biology was discovered by comparative studies inspired only by a curiosity about the structure and development of wild animals. There is no reason to doubt that many other species, as yet unknown to laboratory biologists, have peculiarities that would make them particularly amenable to certain kinds of investigation. The discovery of new experimental organisms is as important to the progress of science as new techniques and instruments. Having the breadth of knowledge to identify suitable species is by itself an important reason for studying comparative biology.

Zoos as well as laboratories have made enormous progress in breeding and maintaining organisms in captivity, but even so, only a tiny minority of all species has been successfully studied under controlled conditions. It is not just large, rare or inaccessible organisms, such as whales and trees, that are not amenable to study in the laboratory; many microbes are also intractable. Our understanding of their structure and metabolism has to be based largely on inferences from where and when they occur naturally, and their associations with other species.

Convenience of maintenance is also an important reason for the choice of bakers' yeast, *Saccharomyces cerevisiae*, over thousands of other species of fungi. For at least 5000 years, people have bred *Saccharomyces* 'in captivity' to leaven dough and brew beer, but since the 1940s, yeast has had an entirely new role as a laboratory organism. This hardy, fast-growing, but structurally simple eukaryote has a surprisingly intricate sex life that has been exploited for studies of gene structure, the control of cell division and many other topics in molecular biology and genetics.

It is important to remember that there is no such thing as an 'average' or 'general' laboratory organism which somehow represents all the others in every respect. All species have unique features and capabilities that enable them to survive and prosper in the wild. Biologists simply exploit organisms whose structure, habits and habitats lend themselves to being adapted to laboratory situations. Research based upon observations and comparison usually involves an even wider range of organisms than that which is primarily experimental, but data from many laboratory species first used for experiments are integrated into comparative studies.

SUMMARY OF SECTION 3.5

1   Species are chosen for intensive study in the laboratory because of their short life cycle, convenience of maintenance and feeding, and certain features of their anatomy, physiology or genetics.

2   *Drosophila* was bred for genetics research nearly a century ago because it is easy to breed in captivity, has few chromosomes and a complex body structure that is easily quantified. It later proved suitable for studying many aspects of cell biology and behaviour. Polytene chromosomes were observed and studied by microscopists long before cell biologists developed methods for studying them experimentally.

3   The stereotyped cell structure and behaviour of nematodes make them suitable for cell biology research. *Caenorhabditis* is transparent, non-parasitic and easy to breed in artificial conditions.

4   Rats and mice are the most closely related to humans of the widely used laboratory organisms. They share our diet and many of our pathogens. Mice are the only higher animals in which the selective elimination of particular genes works well.

5   Being haploid and proliferating very rapidly, bacteria such as *E. coli* are ideal for studying the basic mechanisms of genetics, protein synthesis and energy metabolism.

6   The small genome and short life cycle of *Arabidopsis* offers many technical advantages for plant genetics and molecular biology.

7   Advances in knowledge of organisms in the wild and of husbandry techniques underpin the exploitation of many other organisms that are suited to investigating certain topics.

3.6 PLANNING AND INTERPRETING EXPERIMENTS

In *C. elegans*, every cell is identified by its appearance and/or position in the worm (see Section 3.5.2) so, at least in theory, each cell, or a known group of cells, can be studied individually. Thousands of identical specimens can be bred, from which exactly homologous cells or tissues can be taken. But most multicellular organisms have many more cells, and their number and exact position differ between individuals. Biochemical reagents are expensive and many are potentially harmful, so most assays are designed to work well with only small quantities of tissue, rarely more than 1 g and often only a few milligrams. All conclusions about the composition and properties of a tissue or whole organ have to be based on measurements made on samples. In many cases, the samples amount to only a tiny fraction of the whole, especially if they are taken from living individuals by biopsy, so it is essential to assess carefully their validity as representatives of the entire tissue, as illustrated by the following example.

3.6.1 TAKING SAMPLES

Adipose tissue is unique to vertebrates and is most complex in mammals. It consists largely of cells called adipocytes whose size is easily measured with a light microscope, because they are nearly spherical. Adipocyte size depends on fatness, site of origin and other factors, but those of adult mammals are around 1 nl in volume, or about 1 µg in mass.

○ How many adipocytes are present in an adult man or woman of slim build who weighs 70 kg, of which about 14.3% is adipose tissue?

● 14.3% of 70 kg = 10 kg = 10 000 (10^4) g. If each adipocyte weighs 1 µg, a gram of adipose tissue contains about one million (10^6) of them. So a person contains $10^4 \times 10^6 = 10^{10}$ (ten billion) adipocytes altogether.

We know the size of the total adipocyte complement far more exactly for many more kinds of animals than we know the abundance of other kinds of cells, for example those that form nerves, skin, bone, etc. Rats and guinea-pigs have of the order of 10^8 adipocytes, but assays and culture techniques are usually most efficient with around a thousand (10^3) to a hundred thousand (10^5) adipocytes, or between 0.001% and 0.1% of the total. Can we be sure that samples chosen for irrelevant reasons, such as ease of access by dissection or biopsy, are really representative of the whole?

Until recently, such questions were ignored, and tissue samples were chosen at random or from sites that offered easy access to plenty of material. In young rats, the largest and most convenient sources of adipose tissue were those around the kidneys (perirenal) or associated with the epididymes, part of the male reproductive system. Within a few years, the tradition of sampling tissue from these sites became established, and everyone forgot, or never knew, why they were regarded as 'representative' of adipose tissue in general. For many years, few obvious problems with the assumption that all adipocytes were similar emerged. The electron microscope revealed clear differences between muscles from different parts of the body and between neurons in different regions of the brain, but the internal structures of adipocytes all looked much alike. Size is the most obvious difference, which might not matter anyway for metabolism.

Cytokines are a family of several dozen protein messenger molecules that convey signals between tissues, especially the immune system. Long ago, physicians noticed that people and animals suffering from chronic infections, cancer and similar conditions became thinner, sometimes to the point of severe emaciation, and there was a large and sustained rise in the lipids circulating in the blood. An obvious suggestion was that cytokines or other signals from the immune system which was tackling the disease-causing agent also prompted the adipocytes to release their lipid into the blood, from where other tissues take it up and consume it as fuel. But the laboratory data were not consistent with this hypothesis: adipocytes prepared from perirenal depot of rats failed to respond to most of the cytokines believed to be involved in loss of body fat, even when they were applied at concentrations hundreds of times greater than those ever measured in the blood.

The first step to adipocytes making their stored lipids available to other tissues is lipolysis: each triacylglycerol molecule is hydrolysed into three fatty acids and one glycerol molecule.* Either component could be quantified as a measure of lipolysis but, for technical reasons, glycerol is usually more convenient. Adipose tissue does not use large quantities of oxygen, or any circulating nutrient, so (in contrast to more metabolically active tissues such as muscle, kidney, etc.) freshly excised fragments 'live' for several days if incubated at 37 °C in tissue culture solution that simulates normal body fluids. Even isolated adipocytes remain active for several hours under such conditions.

To obtain the data for Figures 3.12 and 3.13, small samples of adipose tissue were excised from freshly killed guinea-pigs, and incubated for 24 h in standard tissue culture solution with or without interleukin 4, a cytokine known to be involved in immune responses. The extracellular collagen was then dissolved away, and the measured numbers of adipocytes so released were incubated for another hour with or without noradrenalin, a substance released from certain neurons that innervate adipose tissue. The containers were gently shaken to bring all the adipocytes into contact with the noradrenalin and the amount of glycerol that each sample had released into the incubation fluid was measured.

○   Which measurements represent the controls for the experiment in Figure 3.12?

●   Those from the samples incubated without either interleukin 4 or noradrenalin.

In Figure 3.12, the lengths of the columns represent the means of values recorded from 12 similar experiments, and the standard error bars at the top of each are measures of the variation of those values.

---

* The details of this reaction are not important for understanding this section.

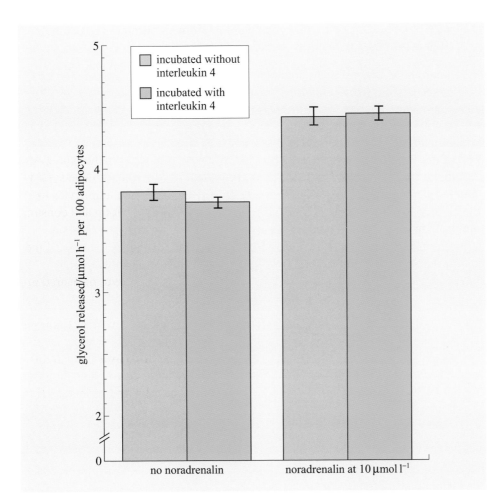

Figure 3.12 Lipolysis from adipocytes prepared from perirenal adipose tissue that had been incubated for 24 h in plain tissue culture solution or in tissue culture solution with interleukin 4, and with or without noradrenalin. The standard errors are shown as vertical bars at the top of each column. Data from Mattacks and Pond (1999).

○ Measure the standard errors on Figure 3.12 and compare them to the means. From these values, how would you evaluate the accuracy and reproducibility of the data shown in Figure 3.12 compared with those in Figure 3.6?

● From left to right, the lengths of the standard error bars are about 0.15, 0.10, 0.15 and 0.12 units. These values are small compared to the means, which range from about 3.7 to 4.4. The accuracy of the measurements in Figure 3.12 is likely to be better than that of Figure 3.6 because the variation of values is small, although one might expect it to be larger since the data come from 12 replicates, compared to only two for the *Hydra* data.

We can therefore be very confident that this experiment is reproducible. The low variation in the measurements suggests that the differences between the mean values indicate real, biological changes, and are unlikely to have arisen from sampling errors, inaccurate assays or some other irrelevant feature of the experiment itself. As a rule of thumb, if the standard errors do not overlap at all, the differences between the means are likely to be significant.

○ Using this principle, what can you conclude from Figure 3.12 about the action of noradrenalin and interleukin 4 on adipocytes?

● Noradrenalin can stimulate lipolysis in these adipocytes, and pre-incubation with or without interleukin 4 has no effect on the aspect of adipocyte metabolism measured in this experiment.

Noradrenalin increases lipolysis by less than 20% whether or not interleukin 4 is present ($(4.4 − 3.8)/3.8 = 0.16$ and $(4.4 − 3.7)/3.7 = 0.19$ respectively). By seeming to show that interleukin 4 did not promote glycerol release from adipocytes, these data cast serious doubt on this hypothesis about the mechanism of weight loss that so frequently accompanies chronic disease. The paradox remained unresolved until measurements such as those summarized in Figure 3.13 were made. The procedures were identical to those of Figure 3.12, except that the adipocytes were obtained from another adipose depot, the popliteal, in the same animals.

Figure 3.13 Lipolysis from adipocytes prepared from adipose tissue from two defined sites (1 and 2) about 1 cm apart in the small popliteal depot between the muscle of the hind leg which had been incubated for 24 h in plain tissue culture solution or in tissue culture solution with interleukin 4, with or without noradrenalin. Data from Mattacks and Pond (1999).

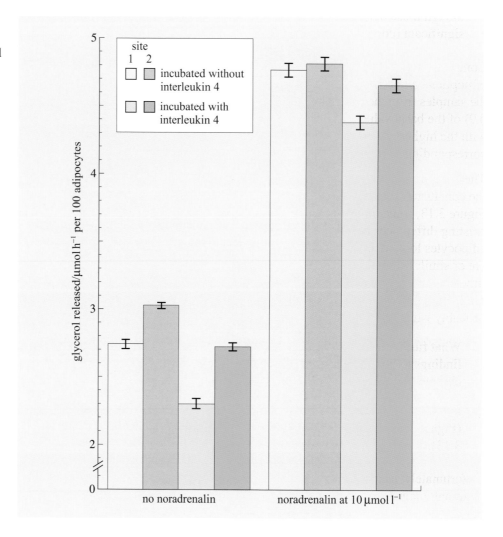

You can see that the standard errors are about the same in both Figures 3.12 and 3.13. The action of noradrenalin on the samples reported in Figure 3.13 is even greater than for those in Figure 3.12. If the differences between the latter were highly significant, then those of Figure 3.13 would be as well, but the action of interleukin 4 on similar samples exposed to the same amount of noradrenalin, and differences between the two samples that were treated in exactly the same way, require further statistical analysis.

○   From inspection of the standard error bars, what can you conclude from Figure 3.13 about the action of interleukin 4 on popliteal adipocytes? How does this conclusion differ from that from Figure 3.12?

●   Lipolysis from these adipocytes is suppressed by interleukin 4, and site 1 is more sensitive than site 2. This conclusion contradicts that from Figure 3.12, which shows no action of interleukin 4. There are large differences between the two samples incubated without noradrenalin (the four bars on the left), but the addition of noradrenalin reduces the differences between them, though those obtained after pre-incubation with interleukin 4 are probably significant (compare seventh and eighth bars).

Comparison of Figure 3.13 with Figure 3.12 shows that lipolysis in both samples of popliteal adipocytes is much more strongly stimulated by noradrenalin than in the samples from the perirenal depot, increasing by up to 90% ($(4.37 - 2.3)/2.3 = 0.9$) of the basal values. These properties produce a much wider range of values, with the highest rate being more than double the lowest measured from the corresponding samples.

These experiments show that the source of the tissue sample is a major factor in the conclusions drawn from the responses to the experimental treatments. In Figure 3.13, some of the experimentally induced changes are as great as pre-existing differences between samples taken from sites only 1 cm apart. All these adipocytes look identical, both as living cells and when fixed and stained, they are of similar chemical composition and share many biochemical properties. But tiny differences in which kinds of messenger molecules the cells are equipped to bind with, greatly influence their responses to experimental treatments, and hence probably what they can do in the living animal.

○   What further information would you need to assess the relevance of these findings to body weight loss and overall reduction in adipose tissue in chronic disease?

●   Find out how many of the other adipose depots respond as the perirenal does (Figure 3.12) and how many share the properties of the popliteal (Figure 3.13).

Unfortunately, nearly all such depots are small in rodents (and in most other mammals), much smaller than the perirenal. So while there is plenty of the latter in rats or even mice, there is not enough adipose tissue in small depots such as the popliteal to supply a properly controlled experiment. Guinea-pigs grow to more than twice the size of rats (males can weigh up to 1.4 kg). The increased precision achieved by obtaining sufficient amounts of exactly the right samples, undiluted by extraneous material that may not have appropriate properties, has to be balanced against the general convenience of small rodents.

We should be aware that even when cells and tissues appear to be similar when studied with certain techniques such as microscopy, they may nonetheless have important differences in respect of other properties. It always pays to test more than one sample, to determine whether a single source may be taken as representative of the organ or tissue as a whole.

○ How can we be sure that the highest values on Figure 3.13 represent the maximum possible action of interleukin 4 on lipolysis from adipocytes?

● We can't, except by making measurements like those in Figure 3.13 on *all* the adipose tissue. Such checks would be a major undertaking even for small species such guinea-pigs or rats.

But at least data such as Figure 3.13 alert us to the possibility of substantial differences in the responses of similar-looking samples of tissue from different parts of the body.

3.6.2 EXTRAPOLATING FROM LABORATORY SPECIES

Obesity is excess adipose tissue; it is not lethal in itself, but it predisposes people (and their livestock and pets) to greater risk of a wide range of disorders, from breaking limbs to heart disease. However, in spite of a huge range of diets and exercise programmes, there is no reliable, lasting cure for this prevalent and distressing disorder.

Laboratory rodents are the obvious choice of organism in which to investigate the properties of adipose tissue and ways to prevent or reverse its growth. A fundamental question was whether adipose tissue enlarged by proliferation of additional cells, or by expansion of a constant population of cells, or by a mixture of both processes.

Figure 3.14 shows the relationship between adipocyte volume and fatness, the gross mass of adipose tissue expressed as a percentage of the total body mass (to take account of individual differences in lean body mass), in 145 adult guinea-pigs, of two different age groups, bred and raised under controlled conditions. To produce a wide range of fatnesses, some animals were kept indoors in small pens and fed on normal or reduced rations, while others were allowed to run about in a large outdoor enclosure. The data are scattered, with the mean volume of some specimens' adipocytes being almost twice as large as that of others of similar fatness. Nonetheless, the data show some general trends that are indicated by the lines fitted to the points.

○ From these data, what is the principal cellular mechanism of adipose tissue expansion in young adult guinea-pigs?

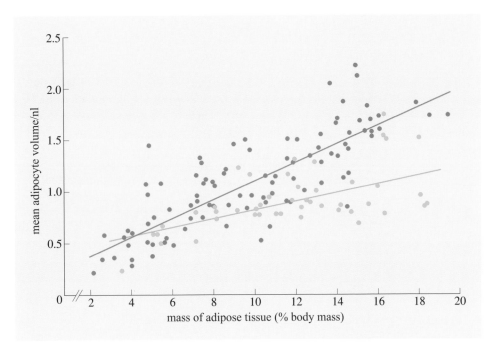

Figure 3.14 Relationship between adipocyte volume (1 nl = 10^{-9} litres) and fatness (mass of adipose tissue as a percentage of the total body mass) in 97 young (4–10 months old) adult laboratory guinea-pigs (greenish brown circles) and in 48 older (over 14 months old) guinea-pigs from the same colony (orange circles). Data from Pond *et al.* (1986).

● Adipocyte enlargement contributes more to adipose tissue expansion than does cell division. A fivefold increase in adipocyte volume (vertical axis) corresponds to a tenfold increase in the proportion of adipose tissue in the body (horizontal axis).

Scientists were impressed by the ability of adipocytes to undergo such large changes in volume. As a result of this finding, research on growth of adipose tissue was directed mainly towards studying the mechanism of adipocyte enlargement and the factors that control adipocyte volume. However, these data show that increases in the numbers of cells also contribute to expansion of the tissue: if a fivefold increase in adipocyte volume corresponds to a tenfold increase in adipose tissue mass, the cells must be about twice as abundant (in proportion to lean body mass) in the fattest specimens as in the leanest specimens.

The total mass of adipose tissue of humans cannot normally be measured directly in the same way as is possible for guinea-pigs, but the proportion of adipose tissue in living people can be estimated approximately using several indirect methods, such as measuring body density by weighing the person in air and under water. Up to 90% of the mass of adipose tissue is lipid, which makes it significantly less dense than watery tissues such as muscle or lungs, or hard tissues such as bone. Adipocyte volume can be measured from small samples of adipose tissue removed during surgical operations or using a biopsy needle. Figure 3.15a shows the relationship between mean adipocyte volume and the total mass of adipose tissue for 279 Swedish adults aged 22–58 years, about half of them people attending hospital clinics.

Figure 3.15 Relationship between the cellular structure of adipose tissue and its total mass in 279 adult humans. (a) Mean adipocyte volume and the mass of adipose tissue. (b) Estimated total adipocyte number and the mass of adipose tissue. Men: blue circles; women: red circles. Data from Sjöström and Björntorp (1974).

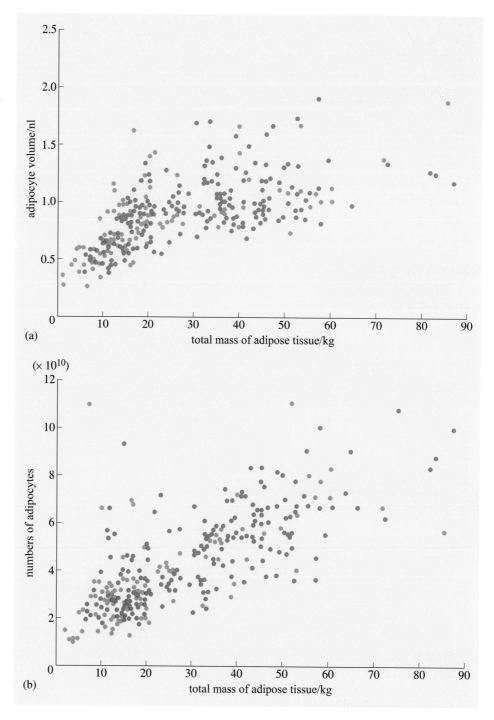

These data are even more scattered than those of Figure 3.14, perhaps because the human subjects were of a much wider range of ages; they probably had much more varied diets and exercise habits than the guinea-pigs; some of those recruited from clinics may have been suffering from diseases that affect adipose tissue. In other words, the 'experimental conditions' under which the humans were living were not as tightly controlled as those in which the guinea-pigs were maintained. The scientists have to decide whether these factors are sufficient grounds for dismissing the variable relationship between body composition and adipocyte volume in Figure 3.15a as spurious, and concluding that the mechanisms of adipose tissue growth are essentially similar in humans and guinea-pigs, or whether to conclude that the mechanisms of adipose tissue growth are fundamentally different in humans, who are primates, and guinea-pigs, which are rodents.

○   How could comparative studies help to resolve this problem?

●   Making similar measurements on other primates and other rodents would shed some light on the issue. If similar data from other primates resemble those from humans but differ from those from all other rodents, the contrasts between Figures 3.14 and 3.15 probably arise from fundamental differences between taxonomic groups.

Figures 3.16a and b show data similar to those in Figures 3.15a and b from crab-eating macaque monkeys (sometimes called cynomolgus monkeys) that had been bred and maintained in captivity.

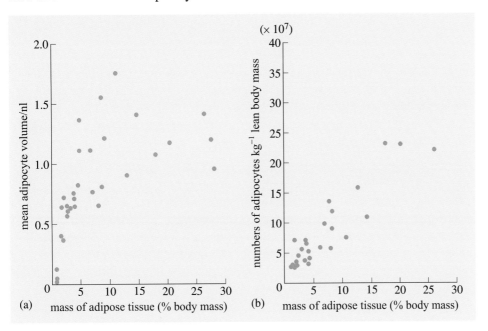

Figure 3.16 Relationship between the cellular structure of adipose tissue and fatness in 28 adult *Macaca* monkeys born and maintained in captivity. (a) Relationship between mean adipocyte volume and fatness (mass of adipose tissue as a percentage of the total body mass). (b) Relationship between number of adipocytes per kg lean body mass and fatness. Data from Pond and Mattacks (1987).

○   What is the principal cellular mechanism of expansion of adipose tissue in these monkeys?

●   Increase in the numbers of adipocytes.

The number of adipocytes per kilogram of lean body mass increases more than 12-fold over a 15-fold range of fatness (Figure 3.16b) but (except below 5% fatness), adipocyte volume is not closely related to the proportion of adipose tissue in the body (Figure 3.16a). However, it is still not clear whether the apparent increase in numbers of mature, readily recognizable adipocytes is due to the formation of new cells (by cell division) or the maturation of pre-existing, immature cells that were too small to be noticed in the leaner specimens.

○ From Figure 3.15, is there any evidence for an increase in the numbers of adipocytes in humans?

● Yes. Above about 15 kg of adipose tissue, adipocyte volume is not closely related to fatness (Figure 3.15a), but the numbers of adipocytes continue to increase over the whole range of measurements (Figure 3.15b), so proliferation of adipocytes must make a substantial contribution to the large differences in adipose tissue mass observed in this sample of humans.

Humans appear to resemble monkeys much more closely than they do guinea-pigs. The uncomfortable conclusion is that research into the factors that control adipocyte volume in laboratory rodents may be irrelevant to understanding the mechanism of expansion of adipose tissue in primates, including humans. Instead of concentrating on adipocyte enlargement, it would be more useful to have studied the factors that control the formation of more mature adipocytes.

○ Would young adult guinea-pigs be suitable animals in which to study this phenomenon?

● No. The data in Figure 3.14 show that the number of adipocytes in young adult guinea-pigs increases at most twofold.

Unfortunately, the adipose tissue of rats, hamsters and other laboratory rodents seems to grow in the same way as that of young guinea-pigs. Studies of these species are therefore unlikely to reveal very much about the mechanism of adipocyte proliferation that seems to contribute so much to adipose tissue growth in humans and other primates.

The data in Figure 3.14 from guinea-pigs more than 14 months old suggest that older specimens would be more promising as animal models of adipocyte proliferation: mean adipocyte volume remained low in some of the fattest specimens, indicating that there must be a substantial increase in the number of adipocytes in these individuals. In spite of these advantages, most scientists are reluctant to meet the additional expense of keeping the animals until they are older. Without major manipulation of the diet or husbandry conditions, even older guinea-pigs (maximum recorded spontaneously developed fatness: 19% of the body mass is adipose tissue; Figure 3.14) do not become as obese as monkeys (maximum recorded fatness: 28%) or humans (maximum recorded fatness: more than 50%).

These limitations of small semi-domesticated species must be balanced against the cost and ethical considerations raised by using primates that are only a few generations removed from being completely wild and need a lot of space and varied food to keep them happy.

CHAPTER 3 BIOLOGICAL INVESTIGATION

SUMMARY OF SECTION 3.6

1 Sampling is essential to almost all field and laboratory research. Duplicate samples from similar sources help to improve the accuracy of measurements.

2 Samples of tissue that appear identical when alive or when viewed under the microscope may not share all properties. Biochemical studies of samples from precisely defined sources may reveal site-specific properties that cannot be identified visually.

3 Comparing similar experiments and observations from a range of species can guide extrapolation from laboratory species to humans and wild animals.

3.7 CONCLUSIONS

The three main tools of biological investigation, theory, observation and experimentation, are closely interdependent. Hypotheses have little chance of becoming generally accepted as theories unless they are amenable to testing experimentally and the data clearly support them as well as, or better than, any rival theory. Appropriate experiments depend upon suitable organisms and techniques, and some theories that were based upon simple observations have waited a long time for the appearance of more detailed laboratory evidence that supports them. We cannot be absolutely sure that new kinds of investigations, experimental organisms or alternative hypotheses will not invalidate theories that we now teach as dogma.

What biologists find depends upon what organism they choose to study and which tissues or organs they examine as well as upon the tools they use in the search. Although many biological processes can be elucidated successfully from studies of isolated molecules, cells or organs, some mechanisms, particularly those involving interactions between several different organs or kinds of cells, must be studied *in vivo*. Invertebrates are often much more convenient than vertebrates for such investigations.

Genera such as *Drosophila* include a great many species, some of which differ only very slightly in structure and behaviour. Comparing these natural 'experiments' provides almost as much information as some kinds of controlled experiment. Comparison of several more distantly related organisms is also useful for assessing the validity of extrapolating concepts developed from the study of one species to another.

REFERENCES AND FURTHER READING

Bateson, W. and Punnett, R. C. (1905–8) Experimental studies on the physiology of heredity, *Reports to the Evolution Committee of the Royal Society* 2–4. [Inheritance of comb characteristics in poultry.]

Carroll, S. B. (1995) Homeotic genes and the evolution of arthropods and chordates, *Nature*, **376**, pp. 479–485. [*Drosophila* genes in modern comparative anatomy and evolutionary theory.]

De Robertis, E. M. and Sasai, Y. (1996) A common plan for dorsoventral patterning in Bilateria, *Nature*, **380**, pp. 37–40. [A modern assessment of Geoffroy Saint-Hilaire's hypothesis.]

Dunn, L. C. (1921) Unit character variation in rodents, *Journal of Mammalogy*, **2**, pp. 125–140. [Inheritance of coat colour in rodents.]

Horvitz, H. R. and Sulston, J. (1990) Joy of the worm, *Genetics*, **126**, pp. 287–292.

Mattacks, C. A. and Pond, C. M. (1999) Interactions of noradrenalin and tumour necrosis factor-α, interleukin-4 and interleukin-6 in the control of lipolysis from adipocytes around lymph nodes, *Cytokine*, **11**, pp. 334–346.

Meyerowitz, E. M. (1989) *Arabidopsis*, a useful weed, *Cell*, **56**, pp. 263–269.

Morgan, T. H. (1910) Sex limited inheritance in *Drosophila, Science*, **32**, pp. 120–122. [The first of many classic papers on *Drosophila* genetics.]

Muscatine, L. and Lenhoff, H. M. (1965) Symbiosis of hydra and algae. II Effects of limited food and starvation on growth of symbiotic and aposymbiotic hydra, *Biological Bulletin*, **129**, pp. 316–328.

Painter, T. S. (1934) Salivary chromosomes and the attack on the gene, *Journal of Heredity*, **25**, pp. 465–476. [The use of polytene chromosomes to study gene action.]

Pond, C. M. and Mattacks, C. A. (1987) The anatomy of adipose tissue in captive *Macaca* monkeys and its implications for human biology, *Folia Primatologica*, **48**, pp. 164–185.

Pond, C. M., Mattacks, C. A., Thompson, M. C. and Sadler, D. (1986) The effects of age, dietary restriction, exercise and maternity on the abundance and volume of adipocytes in twelve adipose depots of adult guinea-pigs, *British Journal of Nutrition*, **56**, pp. 29–48.

Sjöström, L. and Björntorp, P. (1974) Body composition and adipose tissue cellularity in human obesity, *Acta Medica Scandinavica*, **195**, pp. 201–211.

Wright, S. (1917) Color inheritance in mammals, *Journal of Heredity*, **8**, pp. 224–235. [The inheritance of coat colour in rabbits and other small mammals.]

ACKNOWLEDGEMENTS

Grateful acknowledgement is made to the following sources for permission to reproduce material in this book:

CHAPTER 1

TEXT

The Diversity of Life, by Edward O. Wilson (Allen Lane, The Penguin Press, 1993) copyright © Edward O. Wilson, 1993, Reproduced by kind permission of Penguin Books Ltd.

FIGURES

Figure 1.1a: Michael Sewell/OSF; *Figure 1.1b*: Raymond A. Mendez/OSF; *Figure 1.1e*: R. L. Manuel/OSF; *Figure 1.1f*: Michael Fogden/OSF; *Figure 1.1g*: Paul Franklin/OSF; *Figure 1.3*: Higgins, L. G. and Driley, N. (1975), *A Field Guide to the Butterflies of Britain and Europe,* HarperCollins, illustrations by Brian Hargreaves; *Figure 1.7*: McLintock, D. and Fitter, R. S. R., *The Pocket Guide to Wild Flowers*, illustrations by Dorothy Rose; *Figure 1.13a*: CNRI/ Science Photo Library; *Figure 1.13b*: Science Pictures Ltd/OSF; *Figure 1.13c*: Courtesy of Professor Dr. K. O. Stetter and Dr. Reinhard Rachel, University of Regensburg, Microbiology; *Figure 1.13d*: Courtesy of Professor Dr. K. O. Stetter and Dr. Reinhard Rachel, University of Regensburg, Microbiology; *Figure 1.17*: Margulis, L. and Schwartz, K. V. (1982), *Five Kingdoms: An illustrated guide to the phyla of life on Earth,* 2nd edn, W. H. Freeman & Company Limited; *Figure 1.20a*: Taken from the book *Freshwater Algae: Their microscopic world explored*, Canter-Lund and Lund (1995), Biopress, Bristol; *Figure 1.20b*: Eye of Science/Science Photo Library; *Figure 1.20c*: Gordan F. Leedale, Biophoto Associates; *Figure 1.22*: Courtesy of Lynne Margulis; *Figure 1.23*: Norman R. Pace/reprinted by permission from *Nature*, **362**, p. 240, © 1993, Macmillan Magazines Limited; *Figure 1.32*: Courtesy of Dr. J. E. Bebbington FRPS (Field Studies Council); *Figure 1.41*: A. H. Knoll/reprinted by permission from *Nature* (www.nature.com), **391**, p. 556, © 1998, Macmillan Magazines Limited.

CHAPTER 2

FIGURES

Figure 2.2a: Dr. David Patterson/Science Photo Library; *Figure 2.2c*: Adapted fron Margulis, L. and Schwartz, K. V. (1998), *Five Kingdoms: An illustrated guide to the phyla of life on Earth,* 3rd edn, W. H. Freeman & Company Limited; *Figure 2.6*: Brusca, R. C. and Brusca, G. J. (1990), *Invertebrates*, Sinauer Associates, Inc.; Figures *2.10, 2.20, 2.21a*: Taken from the book *Freshwater Algae: Their microscopic world explored*, Canter-Lund and Lund (1995), Publishers Biopress, Bristol; *Figure 2.23b*: Adapted from Brusca, R. C. and Brusca, G. J. (1990), *Invertebrates*, Sinauer Associates, Inc.

CHAPTER 3

FIGURES

Figure 3.1: Mansell Collection/Time Inc; *Figure 3.2*: Science Museum/Science and Society Picture Library; *Figure 3.3*: Phototheque de musée de l'Homme; *Figure 3.5*: Heather Angel, Biofotos; *Figure 3.7*: David Scarf, Science Photo Library; *Figure 3.6*: Muscatine, L. and Lenhoff, H. M. (1965) *Biological Bulletin*, **129**, pp. 316–328; *Figure 3.8*: Courtesy of Robert Saunders; *Figure 3.9*: Courtesy of Caroline M. Pond; *Figure 3.10*: Nottingham *Arabidopsis* Stock Centre; *Figure 3.11*: Science Photo Library; *Figure 3.12:* Mattacks, C. A. and Pond, C. M. (1999) *Cytokine*, **11**, pp. 334–346; *Figure 3.13:* Mattacks, C. A. and Pond, C. M. (1999) *Cytokine*, **11**, pp. 334–346; *Figure 3.14*: Adapted from (1986) *British Journal of Nutrition*, CAB International; *Figure 3.15a,b*: Sjostrom, L. and Bjorntorp, P. Adapted from (1974) *Acta Med Scand*, **195**; *Figure 3.16*: Pond, C. M. and Mattacks, C. A. (1987) *Folia Primatologica* **48**, pp. 164–185.

INDEX

Note: Entries in **bold** are key terms. Page numbers referring to information that is given only in a figure or caption are printed in *italics*.

A

Acetabularia sp. 71, 77

Actinomycota (actinomycetes) 27, *28*

Actinophrys sol 68

Actinopoda (actinopods) 68, 70, *71*, 73, 74

adipocytes
    sampling for experiments 119–24
    volume related to fatness 124–8

aerobic metabolism, evolution 58, 60, 69

agar 73

Agaricus sp. *44*

Agrostis capillaris (common bent-grass), heavy-metal
    tolerance 4–5

algae 30, 33, *34*, 35, 63, 68
    multicellular 68, 78–80, 81, 87–9
    symbiotic relationships 90, 100–3, 104

Alouatta seniculus (red howler monkey) *3*

alternation of generations 36, 87, 88–9

Amoeba proteus 65, 68

amoeboid movement 64

amoeboid organisms *34*, 67, 68, 70

amphiaerobes 58, 59

Anabaena sp. *27*

analogous characteristics **11**, 88

anamorphic fungi **45**, *46*

angiosperms (flowering plants) 37, *38*, **41**

Animalia (animals, Metazoa) 46–52
    definition 47

Annelida, laboratory organisms *116*

Anopheles spp. (mosquitoes) 85–7

Anthocerophyta (hornworts) *38*

Anthophyta *see* angiosperms

antibiotics
    resistance to 9
    synthesis 27

appendages, homologies in vertebrate *10*, 11

Arabidopsis thaliana (thale cress) 113

Archaea 19–22
    kingdoms 24–5

Archaea hypothesis 21

Archaebacteria *see* Archaea

Archaeoglobus fulgidus 20

archamoebas 65, 68, 70

Archezoa 32, 58–9, 65, 66, 68

arthropods
    laboratory organisms 115, *116*
    relatedness to vertebrates 97

artificial classification of organisms **7**

Artiodactyla 16–18

ascomycetes *44*, 45, *46*

atmosphere 57

autotrophy 22, 62–3

B

bacilli *20*

Bacillus subtilis, genome 27

Bacteria 19–22, 25–8
    antibiotic resistance 9

banded iron formations (BIFs) 58

basidiomycetes *44*, *46*

bent-grass *see* common bent-grass (*Agrostis capillaris*)

BIFs (banded iron formations) 58

Bilateria 48

binomial nomenclature **11**

biodiversity 1–4
    definition 5
    types 3–4

biological definition of a species 7

biological pest control 9

biostratigraphy 74

birds, phylogeny 14–15

bladderwrack (*Fucus vesiculosus*) *79*

blastula *47*

Bodo sp. *30*

body plans 49, 52

body shape 77, 80

body size 70–71, 75–8

bog-mosses (*Sphagnum* spp.) 39

bovine spongiform encephalopathy (BSE) 95–6

Brenner, Sydney 109

bromeliads *3*

broomrapes (*Orobanche* spp.) 35

brown seaweeds (Phaeophyta) 68, 79–80, 88, 89

bryophytes (non-vascular plants) 35, *38*, **39**

buttercups (*Ranunculus* spp.) 11

butterflies *3*, 7

C

cacti *9*
Caenorhabditis elegans 109–11, 117
calcification (algae) **73**
Caligo teucer (owl butterfly) *3*
Cambrian 'explosion' 48
Canis familiaris (dog), classification *12*, 13
Capsella bursa-pastoris (shepherd's purse), embryo *35*
carbon cycle, protoctists and 74
cat (*Felis catus*), classification *12*, 13
cattle *see under* Artiodactyla
cell walls 36, **72**, 73
cellulose 36, 73
    synthesis 62
Ceratium sp. *72*
Cetacea, relatedness to Artiodactyla 16–18
chalk 74
chemoautotrophs 21
chitin 42
Chlorophyta (green algae) 33, *34*, 68, 71, 77, 80, *81*, 87–8
chloroplasts 22, 36
    acquisition by protoctists 32–4, 62–3, 90
    loss 33
choanoflagellates 49, 81
Chordata 49
chromosomes 20
    polytene 107–8
chrysophytes *67*
chytrids 45, *46*
cilia 30, 66
Ciliophora (ciliates) *30*, 62, 66–7, 70–71, 78
class (taxon) **13**
classification of organisms 6–18
club mosses *38*
Cnidaria (corals and jellyfish) **49**
coccolithophorids *73*, 74
Codosiga sp. 81
coenocytic hyphae **42**
coevolution 41, 43
colonies (protoctists) **80**–81
combustion, and respiration 94–5
common bent-grass (*Agrostis capillaris*), heavy-metal
    tolerance 4–5
common horsetail (*Equisetum arvense*) 39
Conchocelis rosea 88
conifers (Coniferophyta) *38*, **40**
conserved molecular structures 15
control experiments **99**

convergent evolution 8, *9*, 27, 45, 74, 88
coral fungus *3*
corals 49, 73, 74
Coscinodiscus 73
cotyledons 41
creeping buttercup (*Ranunculus repens*) 11
Crenarchaeota 24, *25*
cryptonucleus (nucleomorph) 32, *34*
cryptophytes 33, *34*
Cyanobacteria 26, 27, 57, 62
Cycadophyta (cycads) *38*
cysts, protoctistan 69–70
cytochrome c 15
cytokines 120
cytoplasmic streaming 77
cytoskeleton 65
cytosome 66

D

Danio rerio (zebra-fish) 115
Darwin, Charles 98
decomposition (biological) 43
derived characteristics 13
diatoms 70, 73, 74
dicots (Dicotyledones) **41**
differentiation of cells **79**–80
diffusion (intracellular transport) 76
digestion, extracellular 64
dinoflagellates *34*, 63, 72–3, 74
divergent evolution 17
diversity of life *see* biodiversity
DNA, short interspersed elements (SINEs) *18*
dog (*Canis familiaris*), classification *12*, 13
domain (taxon) **13**, **15**, 19–22
Drosophila (fruit-fly) 106–9, 117

E

Echinodermata, laboratory organisms *116*
Embryophyta *see* Plantae (plants)
embryos 35
    animal (fossil) 48
Emiliana huxleyi 73
endocytosis 64–65
endoskeletons 72–73
endosymbiosis 22, 32, 62, 90
    see also primary endosymbiosis; secondary endosymbiosis
Epulopiscium fishelsoni 28
Equisetum arvense (common horsetail) 40

Equisetum sylvaticum (horsetail) *39*
Escherichia coli 20, 26
    laboratory organism 113–14
Eubacteria *see* Bacteria
eudicots (Eudicotyledones) 41
Euglena sp. *72*
euglenoids *34*, 72, 83
Eukarya 19–22
    kingdoms *23*, 29–52
    see also Animalia (animals); Fungi; Plantae (plants);
Protoctista
    origin 21–2
Euplotes 78
Euryarchaeota 24, *25*
exocytosis 64–65
experiments 99–104
    planning and interpreting 119–29
    see also laboratory organisms
extracellular digestion 64

F

family (taxon) **13**
feeding, protoctists 63–8
Felis catus (cat), classification *12*, 13
ferns (Pterophyta) **37**, *38*
festoon butterflies (*Zerynthia* spp.) 7
flagella (bacterial) 27
flagella (protoctist) **29**–30, 65, *66*
flagellates *30*, 65–8
flowering plants (angiosperms) 37, **41**
flowers 41
Foraminifera (forams) 68, 74
fossils
    animals 48
    classification 8–9
    evidence for phylogenies 15
    protoctists 69–70, 74
free radicals 62
frogs, laboratory organisms 115
fruit-fly (*Drosophila*) 106–9, 117
fruits 41
Fucus spp. 89
Fucus vesiculosus (bladderwrack) *79*
Fungi *3*, 27, 41–6
    definition 45
fusion hypothesis 21–22

G

gametes 36
gametophyte 36
gene transfer 9, 27
genera (*sing.* **genus**) **10**
genetic studies 105, 108, 110, 112–13, 114
genetic variation 4–5
Geoffroy Saint-Hilaire, Étienne 97
Giardia lamblia 32, 58, 59
Ginkgo, maidenhair tree *38*
Glugea sp. *59*
Gnetophyta *38*
Golgi apparatus 69, 72
Gram-positive bacteria 25
green algae (Chlorophyta) 33, *34*, 68, 71, 77, 80, *81*, 87–8
ground beetle *3*
gullet (protoctists) **66**
gymnosperms 40

H

halophiles 24, *25*
haptophytes *34*, 73
heavy metals, tolerance in grass 4–5
Hepatophyta (liverworts) *38*
heterokonts *34*
heterospory 39, 40
heterotrophic absorbers 43
heterotrophs 21
histones 20
homologous characteristics 10–11, 13
horsetails (Sphenophyta) *38*, **39**
howler monkeys *3*
Hox genes 108
Hydra viridis, symbiotic relationship 100–3, 104
hydrogenosomes 59, 62
hyphae (*sing.* **hypha**) **42**
hypotheses 94

I

information transfer (intracellular) 77–8
instrumental studies 99
interleukin 4, action on adipocytes 120–23
invertebrates 49
'iron sink' hypothesis 57–**58**

J

jaguar (*Panthera onca*) *3*
jellyfish 49

K

kelps 79–80
kinetoplastids *30*
kingdom (taxon) **13**
'knock-out' mice 112–13
Korarchaeota *25*

L

laboratory organisms 105–18
labyrinthulids (slime nets) 64, *65*
Laminaria hyperborea 79–80
Laplace, Pierre 94, *95*, 100
Lavoisier, Antoine 94, 100
life cycles
    definition 84
    plants and animals 35–6
    protoctists 83, 85–9
lignin 39
liverworts *38*
Lycophyta (lycopods) *38*

M

macronucleus 78
'mad cow disease' 95–6
magnoliids 41
malaria parasite, life cycle 85–7
mammals, phylogeny 14–15
Masdevallia strobelii (epiphytic orchid) *3*
Mastigamoeba 67
mathematical models 98
meadow buttercup (*Ranunculus acris*) 11
mealy-bugs 9
mean 103
Metazoa 47
    see also Animalia (animals)
Methanobacterium ruminantum 24
methanogens 24, *25*
Metrosideros polymorpha 8
mice 111–13
microbes, difficulties in identification 9
micronucleus 78
mineral cycling 43
mineralization (protoctist skeletons) 74
    see also calcification

mitochondria **22**, 26, 58
    acquisition by protoctists 32, 60, 62, 90
mitosis 35
mixotrophs 63
molecular markers 18
molecular sequence data, measure of relatedness 15–18,
    20–21, 23
Mollusca, laboratory organisms *116*
monocots (Monocotyledones) **41**
monophyletic groups **13**
Morgan, Thomas 106
morphology 19
mosquitoes (*Anopheles* spp.) 85–7
mosses 35, **37**, *38*, 39
motility, protoctists 65–8
Mucor sp. *44*
multicellular organisms **27**
    algae 68, 78–80, 81, 87–9
    bacteria 27, *28*
mushrooms 44
mutations 15
mutualistic associations **90**–91
mycelium (pl. mycelia) 42
myxomycetes 45

N

naming of organisms 6, 11–13
natural classification of organisms **7**, 10
natural selection
    body size 75
    theory of 98
Nidularium sp. (bromeliad) *3*
nitrifying bacteria 26
nitrogen fixation 27
noradrenaline, action on adipocytes 120–23
nuclear enlargement *71*, 77–8
nucleomorph (cryptonucleus) 32, *34*

O

obesity, and adipocyte volume 124–8
observations 98–9
    see also laboratory organisms
Ochromonas 67
oomycetes 45, 64, 73
orchids *3*
order (taxon) **13**
Orobanche spp. (broomrapes) 35
osmotrophy 63, 64

ovules **40**
owl butterfly (*Caligo teucer*) *3*
oxygen toxicity 60
oxygenic photosynthesis 21, 22, 26, 57

P

Panthera onca (jaguar) *3*
Paramecium sp. *30*
parasitism 87, **91**, 110
    internal parasites 47, 64
    see also Giardia lamblia; malaria parasite
    plant parasites 35
peat 39
Pelomyxa sp. *59*, 70
    cell division 35
Penicillium sp. *44*
pest control 9
Phaeophyta (brown seaweeds) 68, 79–80, 88, 89
phagocytosis 63–64
photoautotrophy 26
photosynthesis 26, 57
    see also oxygenic photosynthesis
phylogenies 13–18, 20–21
    animals 47–*51*
    Archaea 24–25
    Bacteria 26
    fungi 45, *46*
    of domains 23
    plants 37–38
    protoctists 30–31
phylum 13
Phytophthora infestans 64
Pillotina sp. *28*
Plantae (plants) 35–41
    definition 36–7
    phylogeny 37–41
plasmodium 78
Plasmodium spp., life cycle 85–7
plastids 36
pollen 40
Polystomella crispa 68
polytene chromosomes 107–108
Porifera (sponges) 47, 49
Porphyra tenera, life cycle 88, *89*
potato blight 64
Priestley, Joseph 94, 100
primary endosymbiosis *31*, **32**–33, *34*
primitive characteristics 13, 32

prions 95–**96**
prokaryotic organisms 9, **19**
    kingdoms 23
    see also Archaea; Bacteria
Proteobacteria (purple bacteria) 26
Protista *see* Protoctista
Protoctista 29–35, 45, 55–92
    acquisition of chloroplasts 32–4, 62–3, 90
    acquisition of mitochondria 32, 60, 62, 90
    body size 75–8
    classification 30, *31*, 32
    colonial 80–81
    endosymbioses 32–4
    life cycles 83–9
    metabolism 60–63
    motility and feeding 63–8
    multicellularity 78–80
    sexual reproduction 35, 82–3
    skeletons 69–74
    symbioses 90–91
Protozoa *see* Protoctista
proximate explanations 4, 94
Prusiner, Stanley 96
pseudopodia (*sing.* **pseudopodium**) **65**, 68
Psilotum (Psilophyta) *38*
Pterophyta (ferns) 37
purple bacteria (Proteobacteria) 26

R

rainforest, biodiversity in 1–3
Ranunculus spp. (buttercups) 11
rats 111, 112
red algae (Rhodophyta) 33, *34*, 68, 88, *89*
red beds 58
red howler monkey (*Alouatta seniculus*) *3*
reptiles, phylogeny 14–15
respiration, and combustion 94–5
rhizoids 37
Rhizopoda 68
Rhodophyta (red algae) 33, *34*, 68, 88, *89*
ribosomal RNA 16–17, 20, *21*, 28
rodents, laboratory organisms 111–13, 124–7
roots 37

S

Saccharomyces cerevisiae (yeast) 43
    laboratory organisms 117–18
sampling (tissues) 119–24

Scenedesmus sp. 81
scrapie 96
sea lettuce (*Ulva lactuca*), life cycle 87–8
secondary endosymbiosis *31*, **32**, 33, *34*
secondary plant products 41
sedimentary rocks 74
seed plants *38*, **40**
seedless vascular plants *38*, **39**
seeds 40
septate hyphae 42
sexual reproduction
    in angiosperms 40
    in protoctistans 35, 82–3
shells 72, **74**
shepherd's purse (*Capsella bursa-pastoris*), embryo *35*
shoot 37
SINEs *18*
slime moulds 45
slime nets (labyrinthulids) 64, *65*
Southern Festoon butterfly (*Zerynthia polyxena*) 7
Spanish Festoon butterfly (*Zerynthia rumina*) 7
specialization of cells 79–80
    in colonial protoctists 81
species 6–9
    biological definition 7
Sphagnum spp. (bog-mosses) 39
Sphenophyta (horsetails) *38*, 39
Spirochaeta plicatilis 27
spirochaetes *27*, *28*
Spirogyra sp. *80*
sponges (Porifera) 47, **49**
spores 27, *28*, 36, **44**
sporophyte 36
spurges *9*
starch, synthesis 62
Stevens, Nettie 106
Sulfolobus spp. 24
Sulfolobus acidocaldarius 20
surface area:volume ratio 64, 75–6, 77
symbiosis 43, 47, **90**–91
    experimental study 100–103, 104
    see also endosymbiosis

T

tapeworms 47
taxa (*sing.* taxon) 6
    higher order 10, *12*, 13, 17
    see also specific taxa

taxonomic hierarchy 10, 11–18
taxonomists 6
tests 72, 73, **74**
thale cress (*Arabidopsis thaliana*) 113
theories 93–95, 98
thermophiles *20*, 24, 26
Thermoplasma acidophilum 24
Tintinnopsis 67, 74
tissue sampling 119–24
Tortula muralis 39
tracheophytes (vascular plants) 39
trade-offs 98
Trichonympha sp. *59*
trumpet cells *79*, 80

U

ultimate explanations 5, 93
Ulva lactuca (sea lettuce), life cycle 87–8
uniformity among organisms 5

V

vacuoles 36, **77**
variable data 103–4
variance 103
variation 4–5, 8
vascular plants (tracheophytes) *38*, **39**
vascular system (plants) *38*, **39**
vertebrates 49
    appendages *10*, 11
    relatedness to arthropods 97
Vibrio cholerae 27
Volvox sp. 81
Vorticella 67

W

Wilson, E. O., quoted 1–2, 5
wracks *79*, 89

Y

yeasts 43
    laboratory organisms 117–18

Z

zebra-fish (*Danio rerio*) 115
Zerynthia spp. (festoon butterflies) 7
zygomycetes *44*, *46*
zygote 35